Fishbone Flow

Integrating Lean, Six Sigma, TPM and TRIZ

John Bicheno

Production and Inventory Control, Systems and Industrial Engineering Book
(PICSIE Books)

Buckingham, England
2006

ISBN 0-9541244-3-X

CONTENTS

FOREWORD

by Kate Mackle

The fact that you are reading this book means that you are looking for guidance on how to improve your business. Is the insight that you seek to be found inside the pages of this book, or indeed any book? With the number of publications already available on the subject of lean, hasn't everything already been said?

A quick survey of what's available tells us one thing: early interpreters of what made Toyota different concentrated on bringing to a new audience the models that Toyota had developed to describe the elements of their well-established system. So we can now find many different ways of describing the "house of lean" and its different components: Just-In-Time, Jidoka, Standard Work etc. Many companies adopt such models to represent their own improvement programme: the (*insert your company name here*) Production System. There are many excellent sources of information to explain the tools and systems of lean. However, knowing what tools we have at our disposal does not help us to design what we want to build.

Maybe you have found yourself in the position of many other lean enthusiasts: trying very hard to use the lean tools and getting some good localised results but not making a breakthrough in performance that would emulate what Toyota achieved? Here's a simple but powerful lesson: if you want to get the same result, follow the same process. Toyota did not start with the tools; they did not start with their system. They started with an unremitting focus on how to use their resources to produce as close as possible to what the customer wants to buy now; how to align the flow of production as close as possible to the flow of cash into the business. As the goal of the business is to make money, that makes sense, doesn't it?

If we are producing to real demand, or as close as we can get, it becomes critical to make sure that the flow is reliable. Machines must be available to keep the flow going; the process must be capable of producing right first time; people must know straight away if there is an abnormal situation that might disturb the flow and be capable of responding to solve the problem; we must not use measures that encourage people to act locally in a way that is damaging to the overall flow to the customer. If not, the flow will stop and we will let the customer down.

So if you want to transform your business, follow the proven route. Decide how you're going to **create** better flow, then make sure you can **maintain** it, then determine how to **organise** people and what skills they need to support the system in daily work, and finally define appropriate **measures** to steer the system towards the goal. In following that route, you will find that you need certain tools and techniques to make the changes and develop new ways of working: which tools you need and in what sequence you need

them will be pulled by your implementation rather than being pushed by the drive to use the tools. By being clear about the effect you want to achieve in your flow system, you can make more sensible choices about which tool will cause that effect.

Many companies have found this way of approaching their lean implementation has given them a ***step-change*** in effectiveness and accelerated their rate of transformation. They have also found that because they focus everyone's attention on how to change the daily task of meeting customer demand, the lean changes are seen as being an integral part of the job rather than a bolt-on activity and are therefore more sustainable. I hope that you will also find that focussing on flow gives you new insight into how to change your business and enables you to make the right choices about where and when to use the tools.

Kate Mackle
January 2006

WORLD CLASS: PRIORITIES

Lean Thinking

Systems Thinking

Statistical Thinking

Lean Operations

Six Sigma

Supply Chain

Priorities

Three principal priorities for operations in both manufacturing and service are Lean operations, Six Sigma quality and Supply Chain management. These interlink. They also need to be embedded in a background of three related forms of thinking.

Lean Thinking

Lean thinking is a philosophy not a system or a technique. It is about simplicity, flow, visibility, partnership, and value. Womack and Jones' Lean Thinking emphasises the elimination of waste and the adoption of five lean principles.

1. Specify value from the point of view of the customer.
2. Identify the value stream: mapping is a powerful way to do this. Concentrate on the object not the organisational department. There are three streams to be mapped, the physical flow, the information flow, and new product introduction. In each there will be value adding activities, non-value adding activities, and temporarily necessary non-value adding activities. Improve the first, eliminate the second, and reduce the third.
3. Make value flow. If possible use one piece flow. Avoid batch and queue. Remove all obstacles that prevent flow from taking place.
4. Pull at the customer's rate of demand. Use one, make one. This extends to the full supply chain. Seek to avoid over-production.
5. Seek perfection through continual improvement and the steady adoption of the first four principles.

The family of lean techniques described in this book supports the adoption of these key principles.

Systems Thinking

Systems Thinking, with origins in biology a century or more ago, only began to have an impact on management during the last thirty or so years. It is the basis of process reengineering and the internet. It is also fundamental to Lean, which is ultimately a systems philosophy.

A system is a set of entities together with the relationship between them. Think of a children's mobile – touch one element and the whole thing moves. So it is with management systems. There is ecology at work.

A central tenet is the process view. Think in terms of end-to-end processes that deliver the products and services customers require, rather than vertical departmental "silos". Some processes will be core and some support. The process view is integral in process reengineering, in total quality, in lean thinking, and in supply chain thinking.

Human activity systems generally have a goal or purpose around which the entities or activities are organised. Systems have clients and customers, beneficiaries and victims. They contain resources (people, materials, and machines) which are joined together by information flows to support the goals. Systems contain sub-systems with all the characteristics of the higher level system.

Trying to optimise a sub system on its own is futile and may be counterproductive. Systems grow, decline and interact with their environment; they are only self-sustaining together with their environment; they affect the environment and the environment affects them. Feedback and control are parts of every system, the effectiveness of which has a major impact on the ability to achieve the goals.

The concept of Learning is central in Systems Thinking. Natural systems learn by evolution. Management systems also learn by experience but this may be too slow. They need to set out to learn specifically about themselves, their operations, their processes, and their customers.

Statistical Thinking

Statistical thinking recognises that variation is everywhere. The key task is to understand and reduce variation, to manage it, but it will never be entirely eliminated. Deming said that a prime failure of management was their inability to understand variation. Consider why so many management "solutions" (MRP, TQM, and even some Lean) do not work. Ignoring variation is a big reason.

Statistical Thinking overlaps with Systems Thinking in that both recognise that all work should be viewed as a process, and all processes are inter connected. Data is needed to guide decisions, and such data should include measurement of variation. Avoid "drowning in a river of average depth one metre".

It is necessary to be aware of the differences between common cause variation and special cause variation. Treating common causes as special causes (known as tinkering) can make the situation far worse. Unlearning the deterministic view of the world is a great challenge.

Lean Operations

Lean has a long history, although not called "lean" until 1990. Henry Ford was a lean pioneer at Highland Park. Deming taught the Japanese about waste. Boeing made bombers using Lean during World War II. Taiichi Ohno and Toyota refined Lean over 40 years. Today many of the most exciting lean companies (Dell, Nypro, Johnson Controls, Volvo, Unipart, Tesco, etc) are once again to be found in the West. Yet some are still to start. The time is now short.

Lean has been slow to expand out of manufacturing. But the signs are now strong in construction, in health, even in law firms. The future is bright. Hence "operations" not "manufacturing".

Six Sigma

Six Sigma and Lean have in common reduction of variation and improvement in performance. In operations, variation is the supreme killer.

Six Sigma began in Motorola in 1987 as an alternative to less successful TQM. The roots, in variation, go back to Deming. In

1995 Jack Welsh who supported it at GE gave the concept. Today there is vast experience in both service and manufacturing. Six Sigma is pragmatic with strong links to the bottom line. Six Sigma is based around process and variation, uses well-established statistical concepts, has a clear methodology, and a recognised practitioner route through "black belt" training.

Six Sigma is not just about product quality. It is about quality in its widest sense, quality of process (both core and support), of service, and of product. Ultimately it is about winning and retaining customers.

Quality and Lean are close partners, mutually reinforcing one another. Their future together seems assured.

Supply Chain

"Supply Chains compete, not companies". Today the great opportunities for reducing lead-time, cutting waste, cutting inventory, and improving flexibility through the supply chain are becoming well recognised. Improving the supply chain means, in the first instance, extending the principles of Lean and Six Sigma to all participants in the chain. A chain is only as good as its weakest link. But with that foundation, there are further massive opportunities by calling in the particular strengths of partners, by sharing information about customers, and providing agility at the most appropriate parts of the chain. The internet, B2B and B2C, is the great facilitator.

The world class trilogy is the way forward.

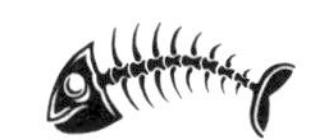

WORLD CLASS: THE BIG FOUR

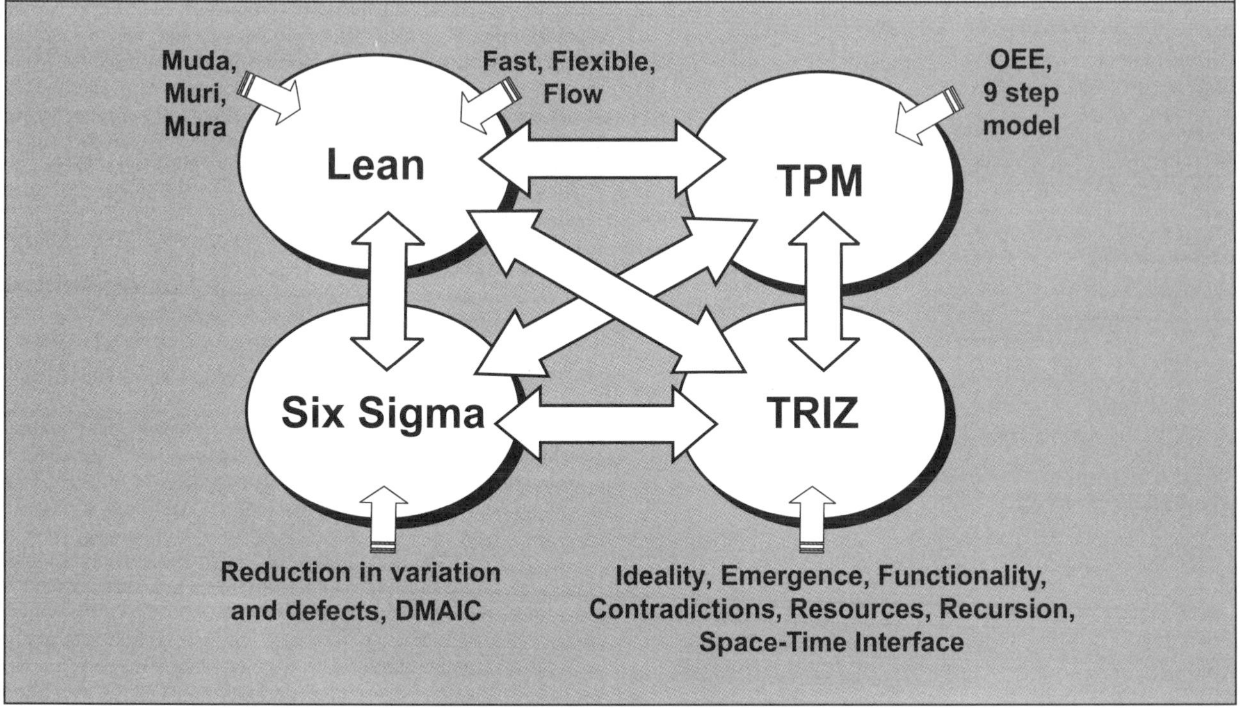

Muda,
Muri,
Mura

Fast, Flexible,
Flow

OEE,
9 step
model

Lean

TPM

Six Sigma

TRIZ

Reduction in variation
and defects, DMAIC

Ideality, Emergence, Functionality,
Contradictions, Resources, Recursion,
Space-Time Interface

World Class : The Big Four

Today, most organizations realise that Lean by itself is insufficient. Lean is needed for flow and waste reduction. Six Sigma is required to reduce variation and defects. TPM (total productive maintenance) is needed to make best use of equipment. And creative thinking is needed for innovation, to enhance value, and to assist with continuous improvement. Although there are many concepts for innovation and breakthrough thinking, TRIZ is almost certainly the most comprehensive.

What follows is an overview – more detail is given in specific fishbone diagrams.

Lean

Lean is strongly concerned with waste reduction. Womack and Jones did the world a great service by highlighting the role of *Muda*, or non-value added activities. Unfortunately, the other two M's of the Toyota system, *Muri* and *Mura*, have been relatively ignored. *Muri* is about 'overburden' or giving both people and machines excessive work. For a person this would include having to work too fast, unsafely, uncomfortably or with poor ergonomics. For a machine it would include being poorly maintained, incapable, or error-prone. *Mura* is about 'unevenness' or working against the flow ideal. It includes encouraging lumpy demand or scheduling, and all the reasons such as poor layout, big batches, breakdowns, and defects that work against smooth flow. It will be noticed that there is overlap between the three.

Lean is also about what Roger Schmenner has identified as the crucial characteristics of world-class service: 'fast, flexible, flow'. Fast because today most competition is time-based. Flexible because agility is needed. Flow because value adding needs to be, as far as possible, continuous.

Six Sigma

Six Sigma has emerged as the best approach to reducing variation and defects. This is done by the powerful methodology DMAIC which stands for Define, Measure, Analyse, Improve, Control.

TPM

Total Productive Maintenance has a focus on making best use of equipment not only through maintenance, but also through improvement. A central idea is OEE: overall equipment effectiveness. The 9 step model has been widely adopted.

TRIZ

TRIZ is a Russian acronym for the 'theory of inventive problem solving'. Today TRIZ is widely used from Boeing to Toyota, from Samsung to the British Treasury. At its root, TRIZ researchers have discovered 40 principles that are at the root of every invention in history. Today it is a gigantic data base. You have a problem; you identify the nature of the problem, you identify the relevant principles; you may explore the data base or just use the principles, you make the leap between the principles and your problem. There are 7 major areas.

THREE THEMES OF LEAN

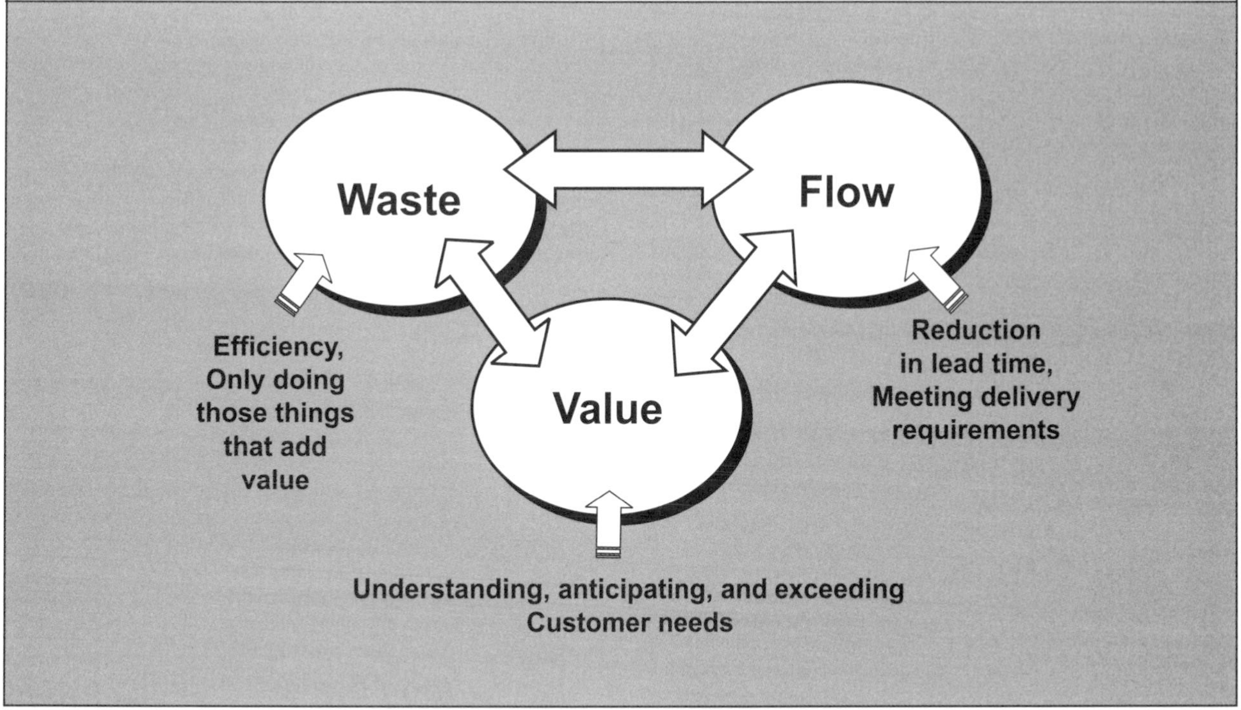

Three Themes of Lean

At its core, there are three linked strands to Lean:

- the WASTE reduction strand, emphasizing efficiency and only doing those activities that add value necessitating attention to customers, value streams, and learning to see waste;
- the FLOW strand, emphasizing reduction in lead time and meeting delivery requirements necessitating an understanding of constraints, layout and barriers to flow;
- the VALUE strand, emphasizing the anticipation of future customer needs and resulting in redesign of product and service value streams.

All three have improvement (Kaizen) and reduction in variation in common, so overlap with Six Sigma, TPM and TRIZ.

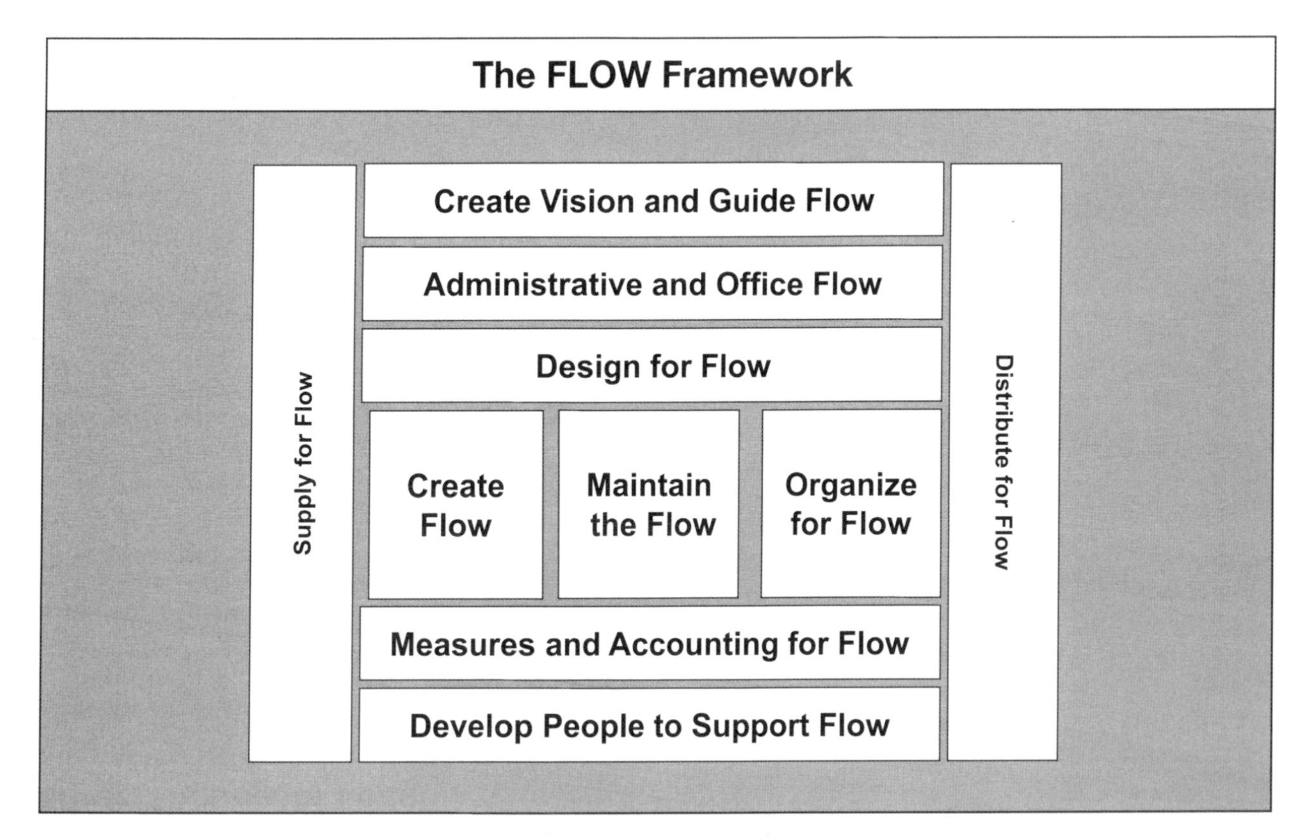
The FLOW Framework
Create Vision and Guide Flow
Administrative and Office Flow
Design for Flow
Supply for Flow
Create Flow
Maintain the Flow
Organize for Flow
Distribute for Flow
Measures and Accounting for Flow
Develop People to Support Flow

The FLOW Framework

This figure leads on to all other figures in the book. Each one of the activities in the flow framework is expanded upon using a fishbone. These are further expanded down to the detail tool level.

The FLOW framework is a complete Lean transformation concept or model, expanded on from top level to detail.

The broad concept is given in the Flow framework figure. A closely related figure gives the essential questions and issues. The figure on Flow implementation gives the central building blocks.

Flow is at the centre. Why? Because Flow is the essence of Lean, once you have identified the requirements of customers. One piece flow is the ideal, but small batch flow or 'keep it moving manufacturing' leads to reduced leadtime, less space, less inventory, improved visibility, quicker problem identification, less rework, all resulting in greater flexibility, improved service and in general greater productivity. Flow is not JIT production; flow needs to be synchronised and end-to-end. Islands of flow are not much better than batch and queue production.

Focus on customer requirements, for leadtime and quality, and on meeting and exceeding customer requirements consistently, and the tools to do so will follow.

So, Lean tools are best thought of as there to support Flow.

Everything you do to implement and improve Lean, from 5S to value stream mapping, is virtually useless unless it leads onto Flow. Creating flow is the first priority. Then Flow needs to be maintained. And the organization must be structured at all levels to support flow. Measures and accounting systems need send out the right signals and motives.

The tools and concepts to create flow are not the same as the tools used to maintain and organize. Unfortunately some companies have lost sight of this, thinking that by doing 5S or Six Sigma or TPM they are 'doing Lean'.

Create flow, Maintain flow, Organise for flow and Measure for flow are the basic four developed by Mackle. The following have been added to Mackle's original framework:

Creating the vision and guiding for flow must be done with the end-to-end system in mind, rather than local 'point kaizens'. Lean should not be about local cherry-picking of tools. Creating the vision and guiding is the prime responsibility for senior management. Without this there will only be local, uncoordinated initiatives, and results will be disappointing.

The figures that follow give the building blocks for each of the elements that lead to Flow transformation. Each of these in turn is broken down into the much more detailed subsequent fishbones.

Implementation Framework

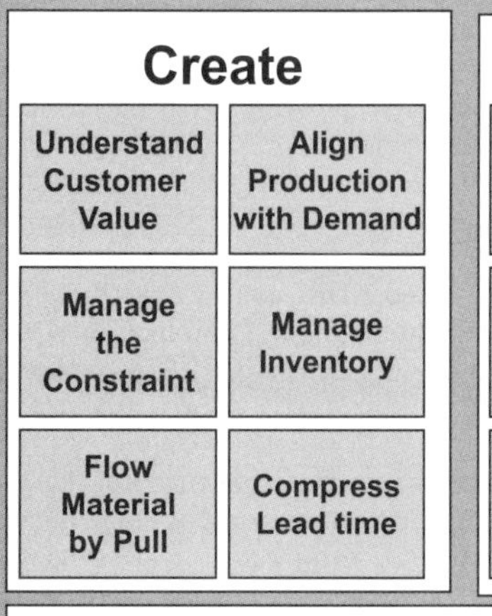

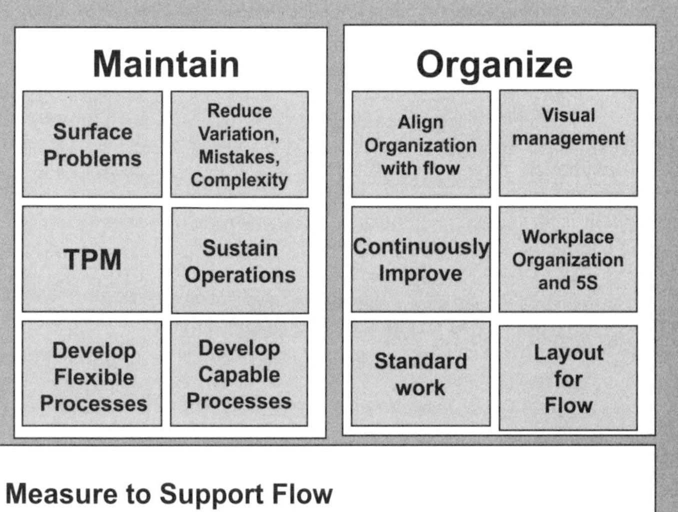

Measure to Support Flow

The Create, Maintain, Organize, Measure Framework was developed by Kate Mackle of Thinkflow

Questions to Ask

Create
Can I produce what the Customer wants, when they want it?

Can I deliver what the customer wants, and replenish according to real demand?

Maintain
Can I keep the Flow going so it does not stop?

Can I maintain a predictable rate of flow in order to achieve planned performance?

Organise
Am I organised to support flow through the plant?

Can I see abnormalities?

Can I react Quickly to resolve Problems?

Measure
Do the measures promote actions that support flow?
Do I know what I need to know locally to support the overall goal?

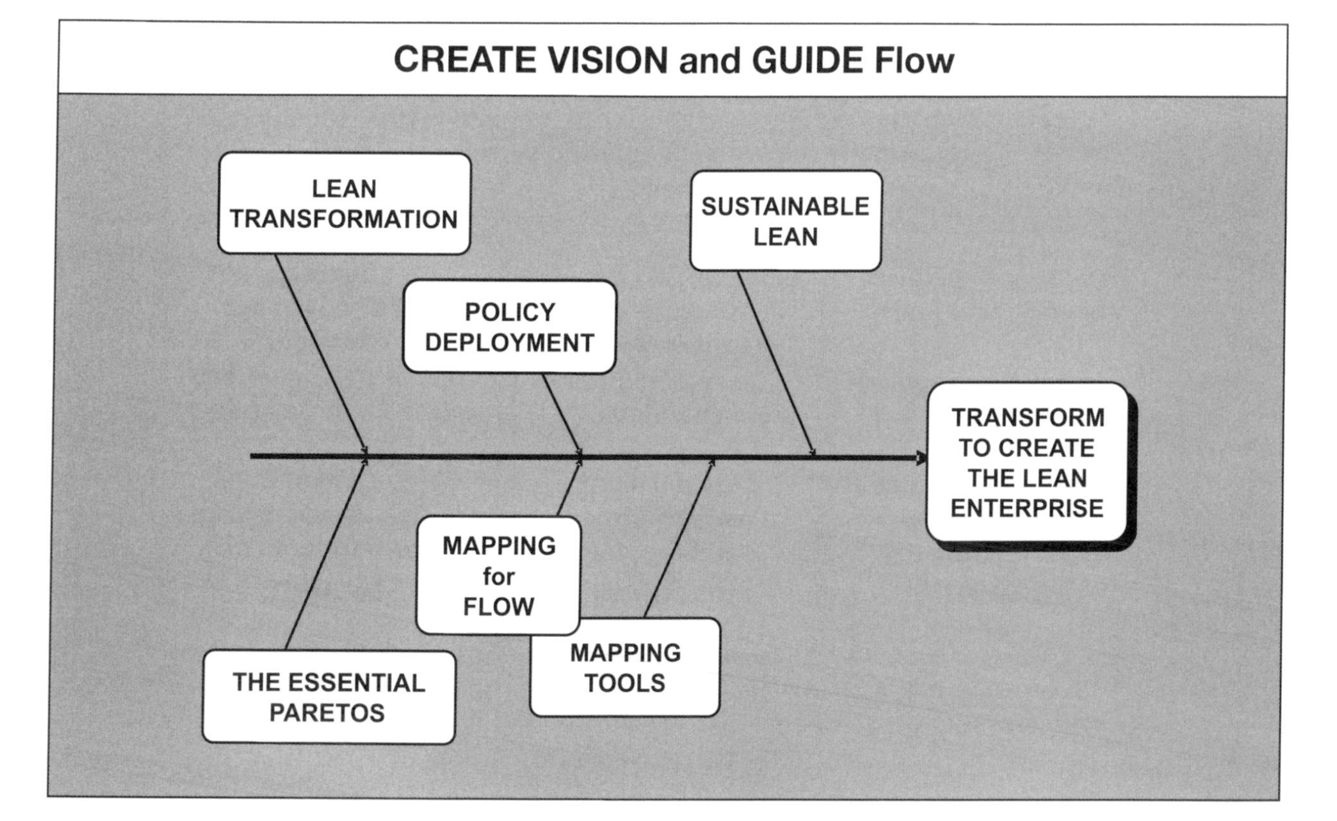
CREATE VISION and GUIDE Flow
LEAN TRANSFORMATION
SUSTAINABLE LEAN
POLICY DEPLOYMENT
TRANSFORM TO CREATE THE LEAN ENTERPRISE
MAPPING for FLOW
THE ESSENTIAL PARETOS
MAPPING TOOLS

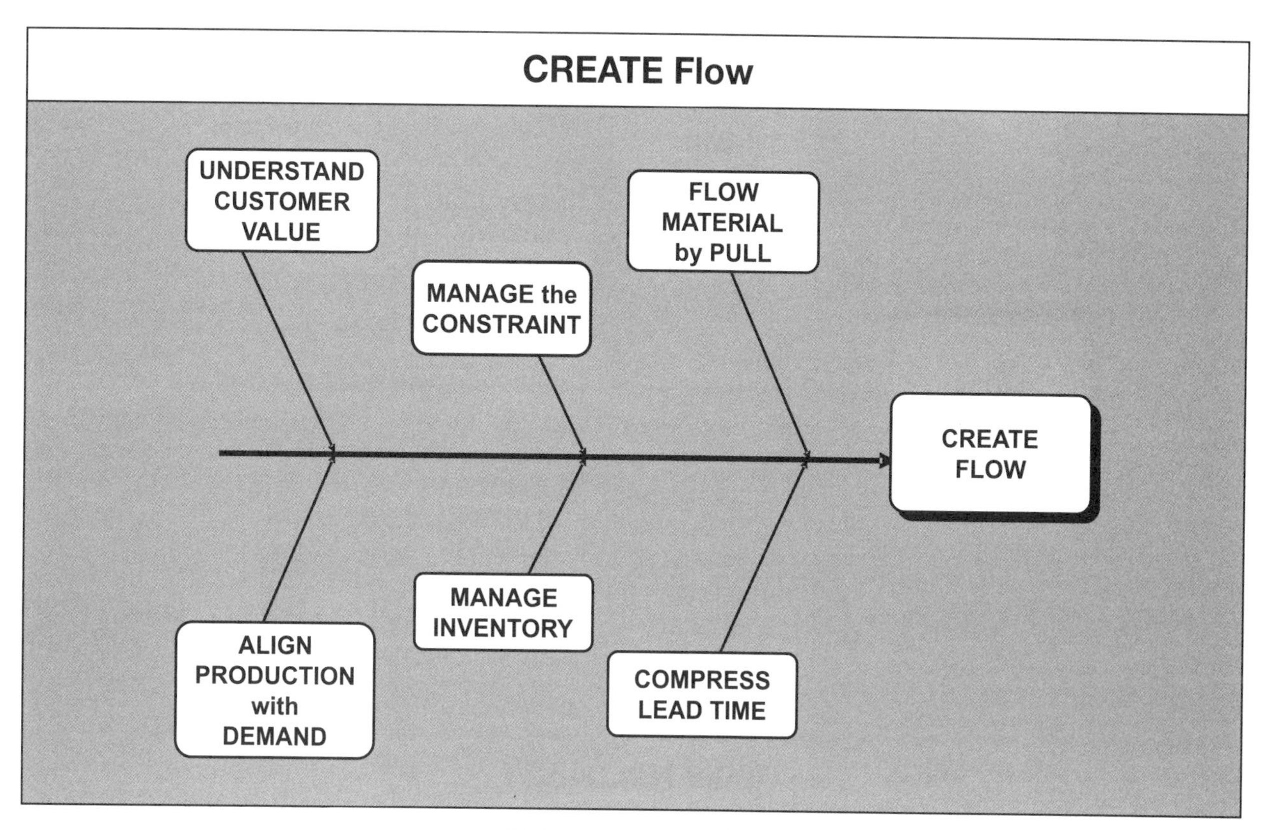
CREATE Flow
UNDERSTAND CUSTOMER VALUE
MANAGE the CONSTRAINT
FLOW MATERIAL by PULL
CREATE FLOW
ALIGN PRODUCTION with DEMAND
MANAGE INVENTORY
COMPRESS LEAD TIME

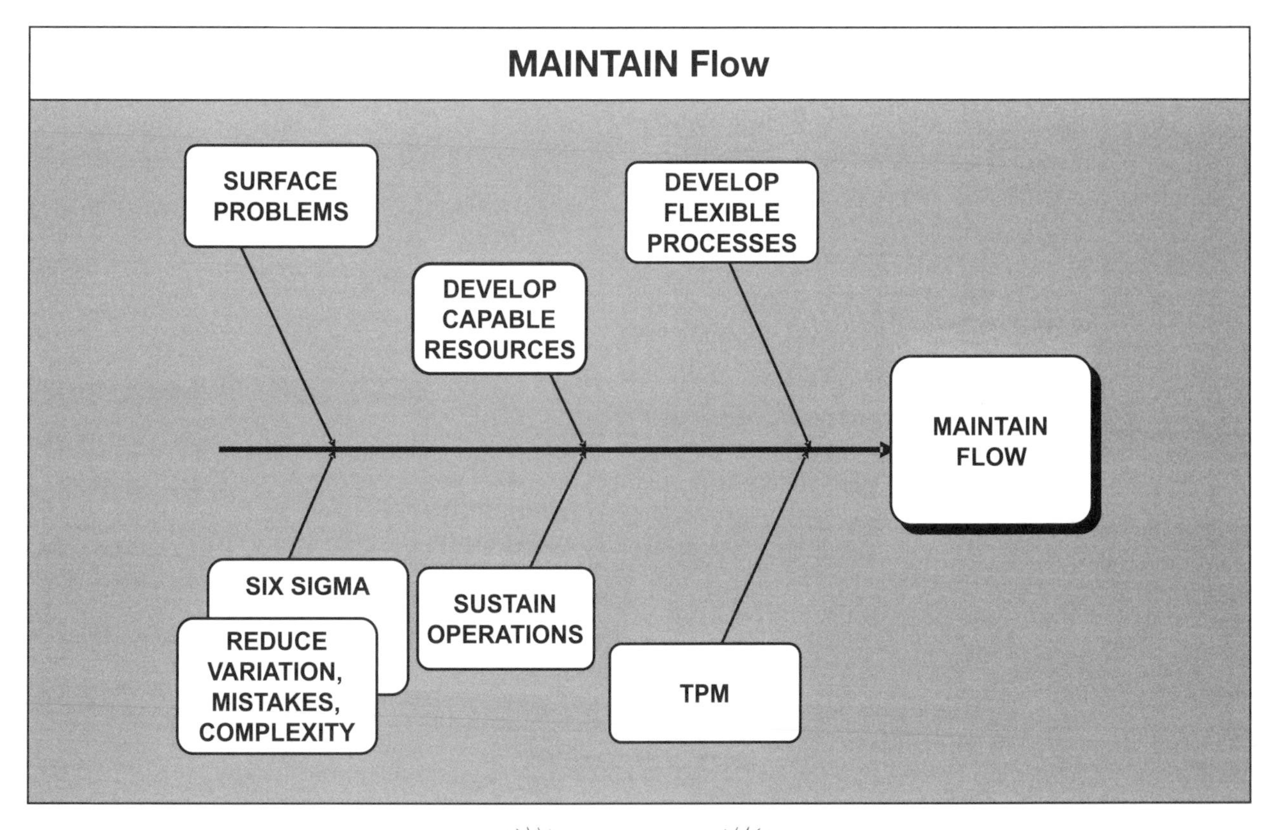
MAINTAIN Flow
SURFACE PROBLEMS
DEVELOP CAPABLE RESOURCES
DEVELOP FLEXIBLE PROCESSES
MAINTAIN FLOW
SIX SIGMA
REDUCE VARIATION, MISTAKES, COMPLEXITY
SUSTAIN OPERATIONS
TPM

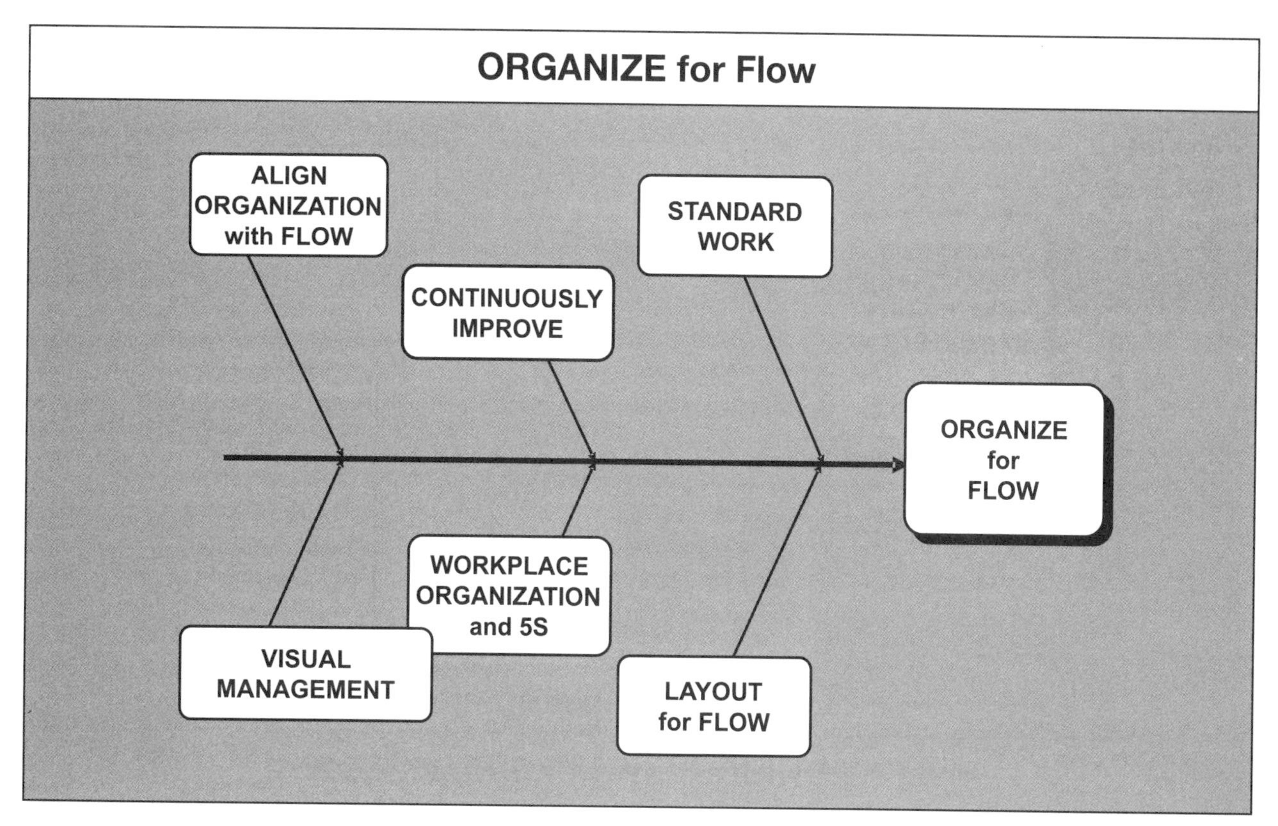
ORGANIZE for Flow
ALIGN ORGANIZATION with FLOW
CONTINUOUSLY IMPROVE
STANDARD WORK
ORGANIZE for FLOW
VISUAL MANAGEMENT
WORKPLACE ORGANIZATION and 5S
LAYOUT for FLOW

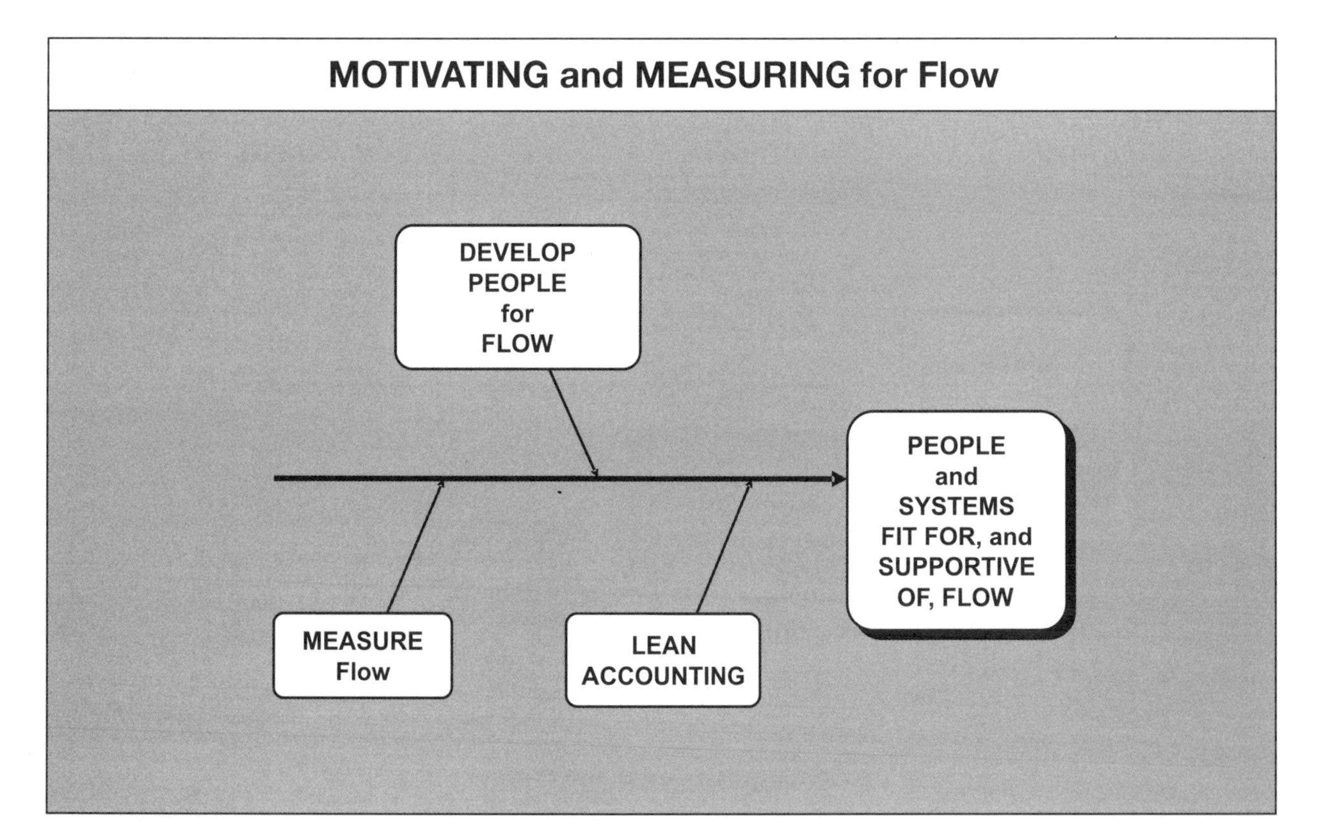
MOTIVATING and MEASURING for Flow
DEVELOP PEOPLE for FLOW
MEASURE Flow
LEAN ACCOUNTING
PEOPLE and SYSTEMS FIT FOR, and SUPPORTIVE OF, FLOW

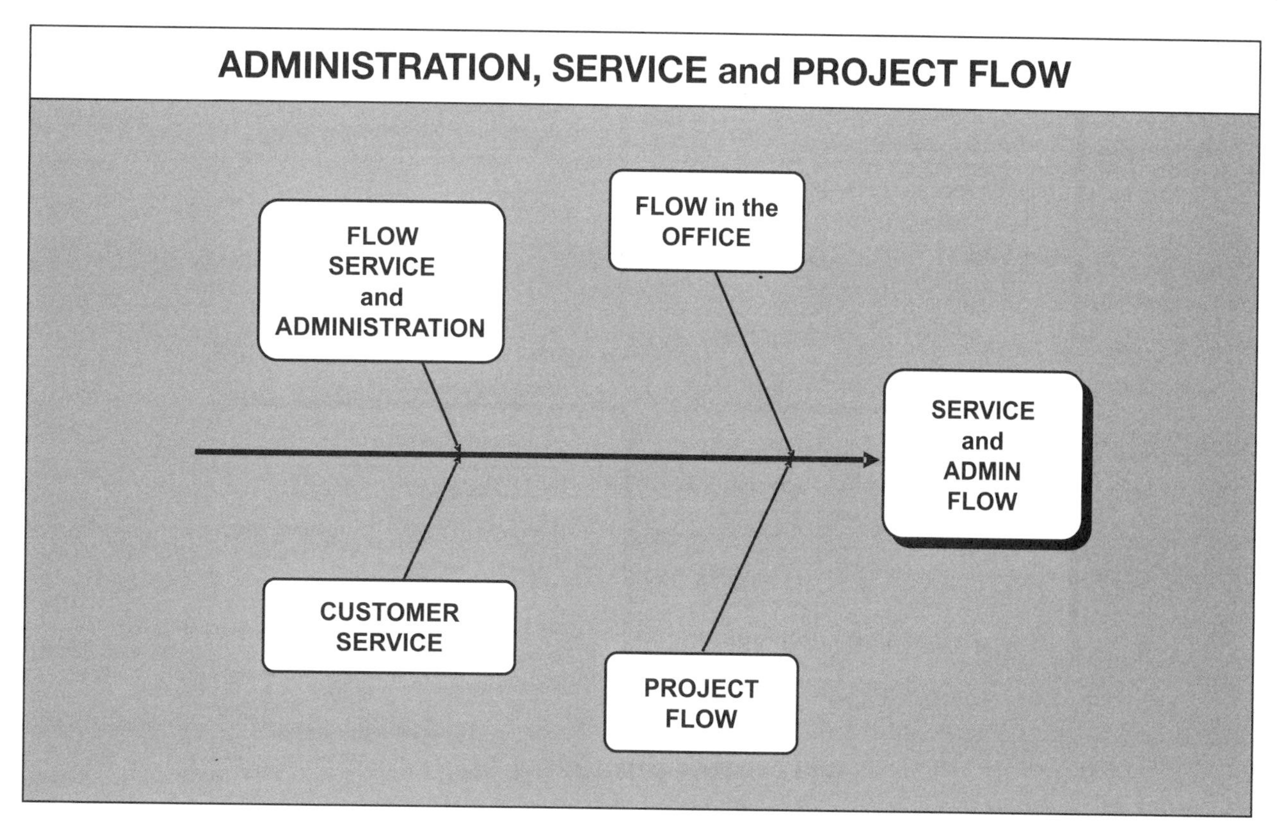
ADMINISTRATION, SERVICE and PROJECT FLOW
FLOW SERVICE and ADMINISTRATION
FLOW in the OFFICE
SERVICE and ADMIN FLOW
CUSTOMER SERVICE
PROJECT FLOW

The Essential PARETOS

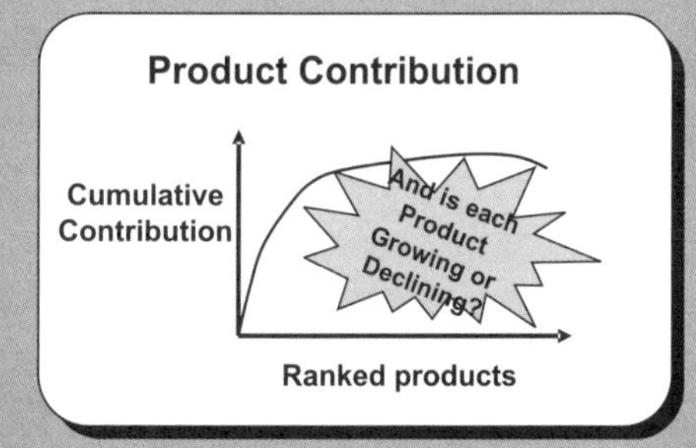
Product Contribution
Cumulative Contribution
And is each Product Growing or Declining?
Ranked products

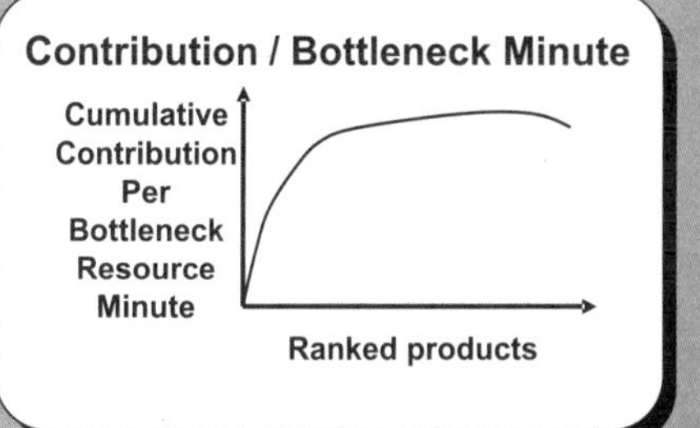
Contribution / Bottleneck Minute
Cumulative Contribution Per Bottleneck Resource Minute
Ranked products

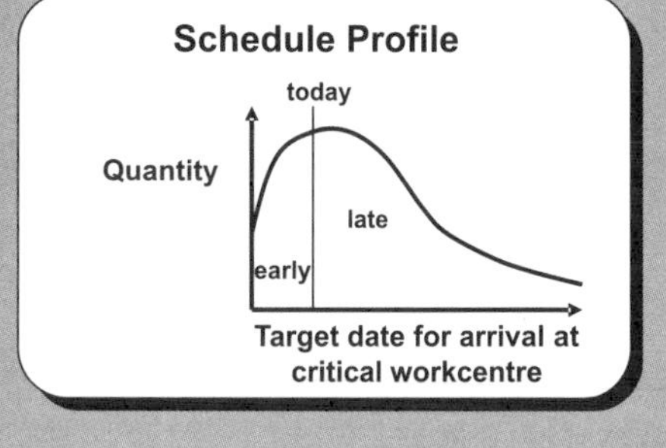
Schedule Profile
today
Quantity
late
early
Target date for arrival at critical workcentre

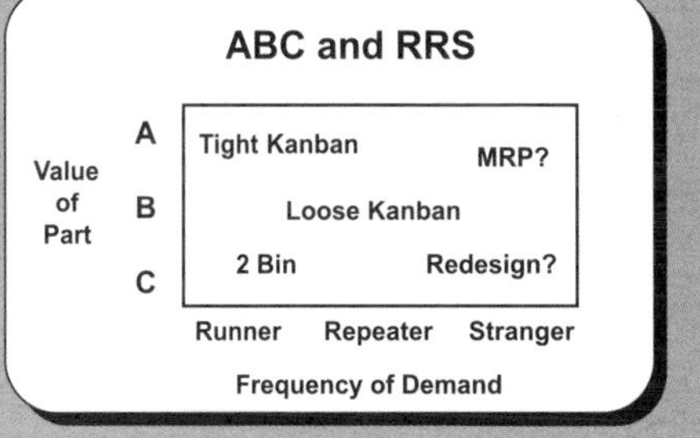
ABC and RRS
Value of Part
A
B
C
Tight Kanban
MRP?
Loose Kanban
2 Bin
Redesign?
Runner
Repeater
Stranger
Frequency of Demand

The Essential PARETOS

There are four essential pareto analyses, that form a powerful set for lean transformation considerations.

Contribution (selling price – direct costs): Arrange products from highest to lowest contribution along the horizontal axis and accumulate contribution along the vertical axis. Frequently a long tail of products that make little or negative contribution is found. Use this to think about product line rationalisation. In companies with important bottleneck processes, do an analysis by contribution per bottleneck minute used. The last thing you want is products making very low contribution but which also tie up your precious bottleneck process. Phase them out.

The position on the ranking of products is not the only indicator. A young product due to make more contribution in future is of course different to a product near the end of its life cycle.

Another variant is to multiply by the volume to give total contribution for each product.

ABC and RRS

Not all parts have the same value – some are A items, some are low cost C. Then there are *Runners* (products or parts demanded every day in reasonable volume), *repeaters* (products demanded at regular intervals but irregular quantities), and *strangers or rogues* (products with erratic demand). Hence arrange a matrix with ABC and RRS as axes. This will be a great aid to inventory and scheduling policy. But, over the long term seek to convert strangers into repeaters and repeaters into runners – by design rationalization and marketing.

Schedule Profile

Develop a standard lead time chart. Then, regularly monitor the inventory at critical workcentres. Ask if parts have arrived too early or too late. Seek root causes. Go to the operation (Gemba) each day and ask. Seek to narrow the distribution so only a few are early or late.

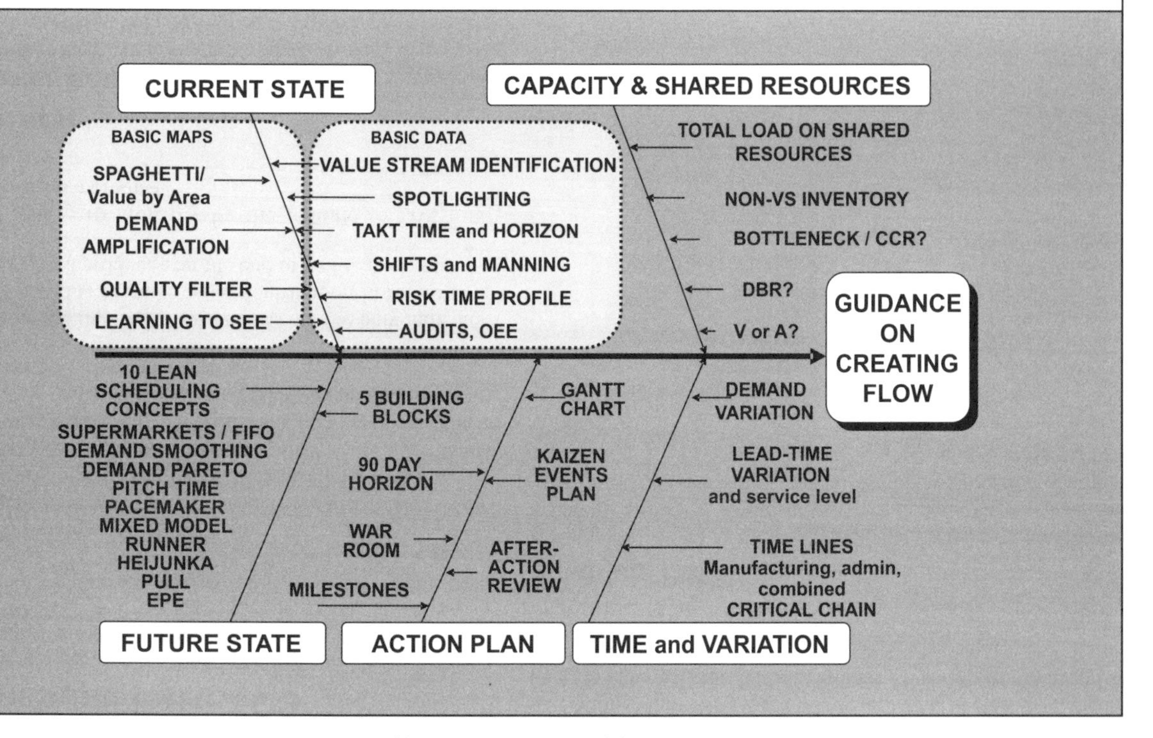
MAPPING Flow
CURRENT STATE
CAPACITY & SHARED RESOURCES
BASIC MAPS
SPAGHETTI/ Value by Area
DEMAND AMPLIFICATION
QUALITY FILTER
LEARNING TO SEE
BASIC DATA
VALUE STREAM IDENTIFICATION
SPOTLIGHTING
TAKT TIME and HORIZON
SHIFTS and MANNING
RISK TIME PROFILE
AUDITS, OEE
TOTAL LOAD ON SHARED RESOURCES
NON-VS INVENTORY
BOTTLENECK / CCR?
DBR?
V or A?
GUIDANCE ON CREATING FLOW
10 LEAN SCHEDULING CONCEPTS
SUPERMARKETS / FIFO
DEMAND SMOOTHING
DEMAND PARETO
PITCH TIME
PACEMAKER
MIXED MODEL
RUNNER
HEIJUNKA
PULL
EPE
5 BUILDING BLOCKS
90 DAY HORIZON
WAR ROOM
MILESTONES
GANTT CHART
KAIZEN EVENTS PLAN
AFTER-ACTION REVIEW
DEMAND VARIATION
LEAD-TIME VARIATION and service level
TIME LINES Manufacturing, admin, combined CRITICAL CHAIN
FUTURE STATE
ACTION PLAN
TIME and VARIATION

MAPPING Flow
Current State

Basic Maps

There are four basic maps (see Basic Mapping Tools figure).

The 'Learning to See' value stream map (VSM) (Rother and Shook) is the prime current state map. This is essential. Beware, however, of pitfalls. Shared resources should be checked out for load and capacity. One takt time may not be appropriate. Have two time lines, one for the shop floor, another for the office. VSM should be done with an eye on the future; there is no point in mapping if huge change is imminent. A VSM is a snapshot; look at the variation over time. Office mapping may be more important. Remember, the idea of mapping is to create the future state and action plan; without these mapping is pure waste.

The spaghetti (or string) diagram should be an essential accompaniment to a learning-to-see. The VSM gives the logic, spaghetti gives the layout.

A VSM gives the situation at a point in time but the demand amplification map helps with schedule and demand variation over time. Plot a graph of demand on vertical axis and day by day over a month on the horizontal axis. Then plot lines for day-by-day customer demand, and throughput at each important workcentre. For flow, there should be minimal amplification or bunching up into batches. Ask why it is not happening: a common reason is a lack of a single pacemaker.

The Quality filter map traces defects and rework across workcentres.

Basic Data and Maps

Value stream identity is breaking the factory into value streams. This may be obvious, but may require product vs process step matrix analysis to identify like products. Spotlighting is highlighting of critical issues not picked up in basic mapping, for example a difficult team, an erratic process, and an impending new product introduction.

Takt time is an easy concept (available time / demand) but over what time horizon, what if there is demand seasonality, what if there is product mix change? Worth considerable discussion! Also, remember that time can be altered to stabilize takt.

An audit helps pick up much information not covered in a map. Examples are Kobayashi's 20 keys, Schonberger's 16 principles. Recommended as an analysis and as a tracking-procedure. Several companies (e.g. Ford, GSK) have developed their own lean audit tools.

Other maps, (lead time profile, detailed process activity maps), may be useful. For some environments, compare month-by-month ahead of delivery date the percentage of orders received

BASIC MAPPING TOOLS

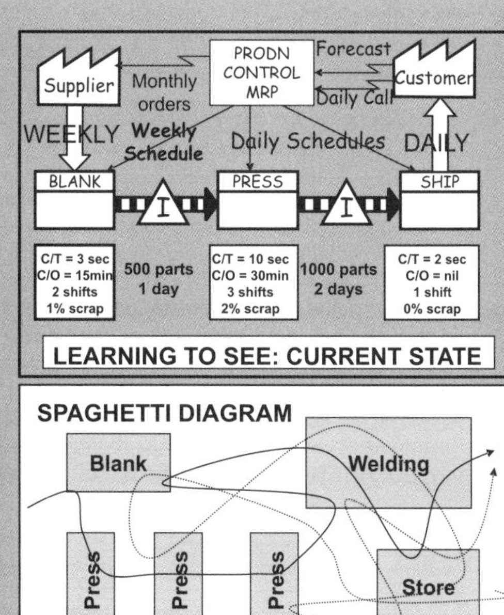

Supplier
Monthly orders
PRODN CONTROL MRP
Forecast
Customer
Daily Call
WEEKLY
Weekly Schedule
Daily Schedules
DAILY
BLANK
PRESS
SHIP
I
I
C/T = 3 sec
C/O = 15min
2 shifts
1% scrap
500 parts
1 day
C/T = 10 sec
C/O = 30min
3 shifts
2% scrap
1000 parts
2 days
C/T = 2 sec
C/O = nil
1 shift
0% scrap
LEARNING TO SEE: CURRENT STATE
SPAGHETTI DIAGRAM
Blank
Welding
Press
Press
Press
Store

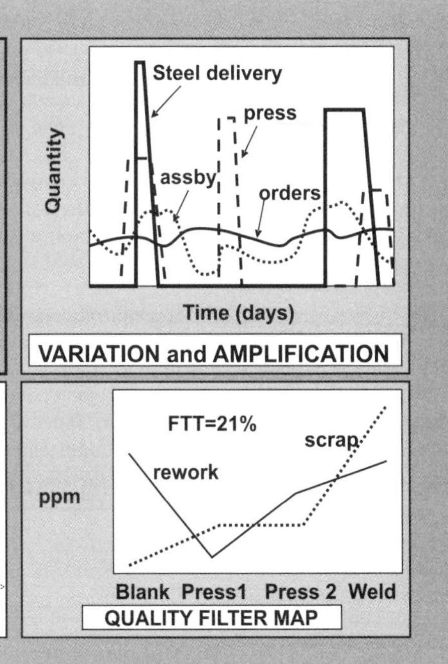

Steel delivery
press
assby
orders
Quantity
Time (days)
VARIATION and AMPLIFICATION
FTT=21%
scrap
rework
ppm
Blank
Press1
Press 2
Weld
QUALITY FILTER MAP

at critical workcentres late, on time, and ahead of schedule. This is the risk profile.

Capacity and Shared Resources

Calculate the load and capacity on resources shared between several value streams. You may discover a bottleneck that needs careful scheduling, perhaps drum buffer rope. A 'V' plant (diverging streams such as a steel mill) and an 'A' (converging streams such as assembly) have different but classic problem characteristics. See the fishbone 'managing the constraint for flow'.

Perhaps the constraint lies with other resources, such as tooling, setters, orders.

Future State

In developing the future state, use the 5 building blocks and 10 lean scheduling concepts. Refer to The New Lean Toolbox.

Action Plan

Work to 90-day implementation cycles, maybe 180, never more. Arrange all maps in a war room. Keep track of progress on a Gantt chart. Certainly have a big review meeting, an after action review, after 90 days to look back and ask how better to do it next cycle. Coordinate the sequence of Kaizen events.

Time and Variation

Be aware of lead time variation not just average lead time. Draw the distribution. Trace the reasons for variation and the percentage of orders not met on time, or service level. Trace both the physical transformation time line, and the administrative time line. Remember Ohno: 'all we are trying to do is to reduce the time from order to cash'.

Understand demand variation. How even is demand? How much demand is 'failure demand'? This is John Seddon's concept of demand that should not exist but does due to not getting things right the first time. Beware of drowning in a river of average depth 1 metre.

What are the sources of demand variation? Self induced due to quantity discounts? Promotions? Seasonality? How best to cope with demand variation? And where should inventory buffers be located: finished goods, part complete (postponement), raw material?

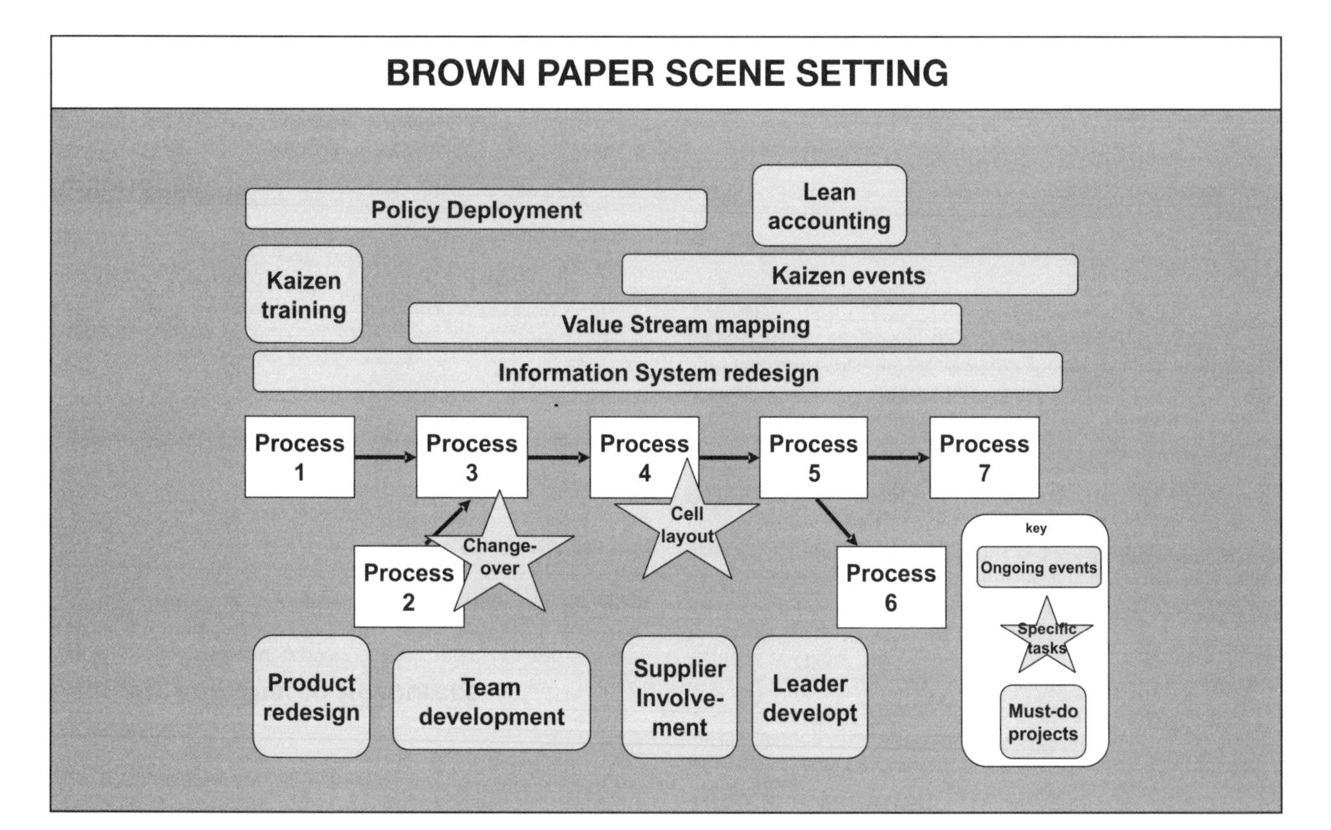
BROWN PAPER SCENE SETTING
Policy Deployment
Lean accounting
Kaizen training
Kaizen events
Value Stream mapping
Information System redesign
Process 1
Process 3
Process 4
Process 5
Process 7
Process 2
Change-over
Cell layout
Process 6
Product redesign
Team development
Supplier Involve-ment
Leader developt
key
Ongoing events
Specific tasks
Must-do projects

MAPPING Activities, and BROWN PAPER Scene Setting

BROWN PAPER Scene Setting

It may be useful periodically to gather key staff for a several-day kaizen event aimed at an overview of priorities for the major value streams on site. Here, draw out the highest-level map(s). Use those as a vehicle for the team to contribute concerns in three areas – projects, ongoing activities, and focused concerns.

An aim is to create high level buy-in, and to see the big picture first before diving in to map specific value streams.

Mapping Activities

Organising: Selecting a steering committee, establishing a Lean Promotion Office (a war office with resources), selecting the lean champion (preferably full time), and lean implementation teams including shop floor staff. A team of around 8 is ideal. Multi-level, cross functional representation is essential. Lean experts must facilitate, not map. Consult the union. Gain agreement.

Pre-Mapping Workshop: Identify what it is that customers value – qualifiers and winners. Identify key processes, product contribution analyses and contribution per bottleneck minute information. Also discuss capacity issues and constraints, identify processes, products and routings to be mapped, and select appropriate data collection periods and frequency. What information flows need to be mapped?

Current State Data Collection: May comprise a situation audit (Kobayashi or Schonberger), and audits of housekeeping status and schedule adherence. Check OEE, standards and inventory record accuracy, delivery performance. Review the measures used and costing system. Collect takt time information. Check on process and schedule variation, and list the possible causes. Check demand variation. Check the variation of lead time performance.

Basic Mapping: Will include the four basic maps - current state "learning to see" maps, spaghetti diagrams, quality filter charts, and demand amplification. Mapping to be done by operators and staff, not the "experts".

Current State Workshop: Present maps and data. Consider possibilities for flow. Check size of buffers and necessity for supermarkets. What are the barriers to pull? How can visibility be improved? Examine existing cell performance and new cells. What are feasible production schedules? One-piece flow? Identify "low hanging fruit" and areas for more detailed study.

Short Term Actions: Probably 5S and changeover, standardisation, possibly selected kaizen blitz events. Identification of short term six sigma and quality improvement projects.

Detailed Mapping and Data: Use process activity maps selectively. Probably map information flows and possibly new

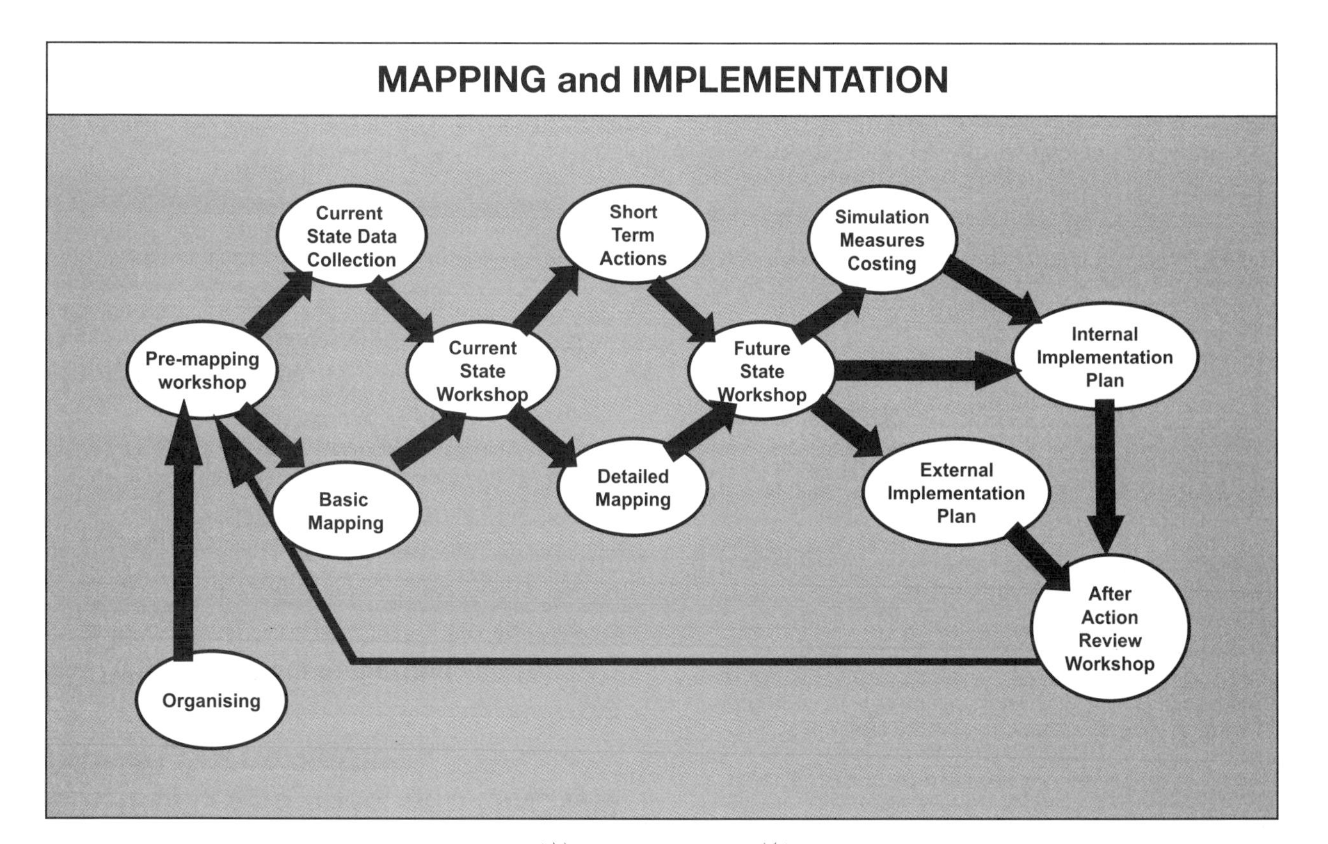
MAPPING and IMPLEMENTATION
Current State Data Collection
Short Term Actions
Simulation Measures Costing
Pre-mapping workshop
Current State Workshop
Future State Workshop
Internal Implementation Plan
Basic Mapping
Detailed Mapping
External Implementation Plan
After Action Review Workshop
Organising

product introduction. More detail on scheduling. Spend time on collecting variation data.

Future State Workshop: Develop the concept. Consider location. Detailed layout and sizing of supermarkets and buffers. Detailed work on the schedule, including the pacemaker process, batch sizing. Kanban implementation plan.

Simulation, Measures and Costing: Possibly small scale trials, scale models. Perhaps even computer simulation. Revise and simplify the costing system. Examine the measures used – see if they conflict. Take time to walk through the implications with accountants and senior managers.

Internal Implementation Plan: Phasing of layout and cell changes. Activities leading to inventory reductions and phased removal of barriers to flow. Operator skill development. Six Sigma project phasing. Develop other plans, probably TPM and information flow. "Small machine" policy.

External Implementation Plan: Plans to reduce demand amplification. Supplier reduction and development. Supplier associations. Sharing information and working towards stable schedules. Phasing in of pull. Other actions such as joint design, B2B, JITII, chained target costing.

Do it all again!

You are on the road but you are never there.

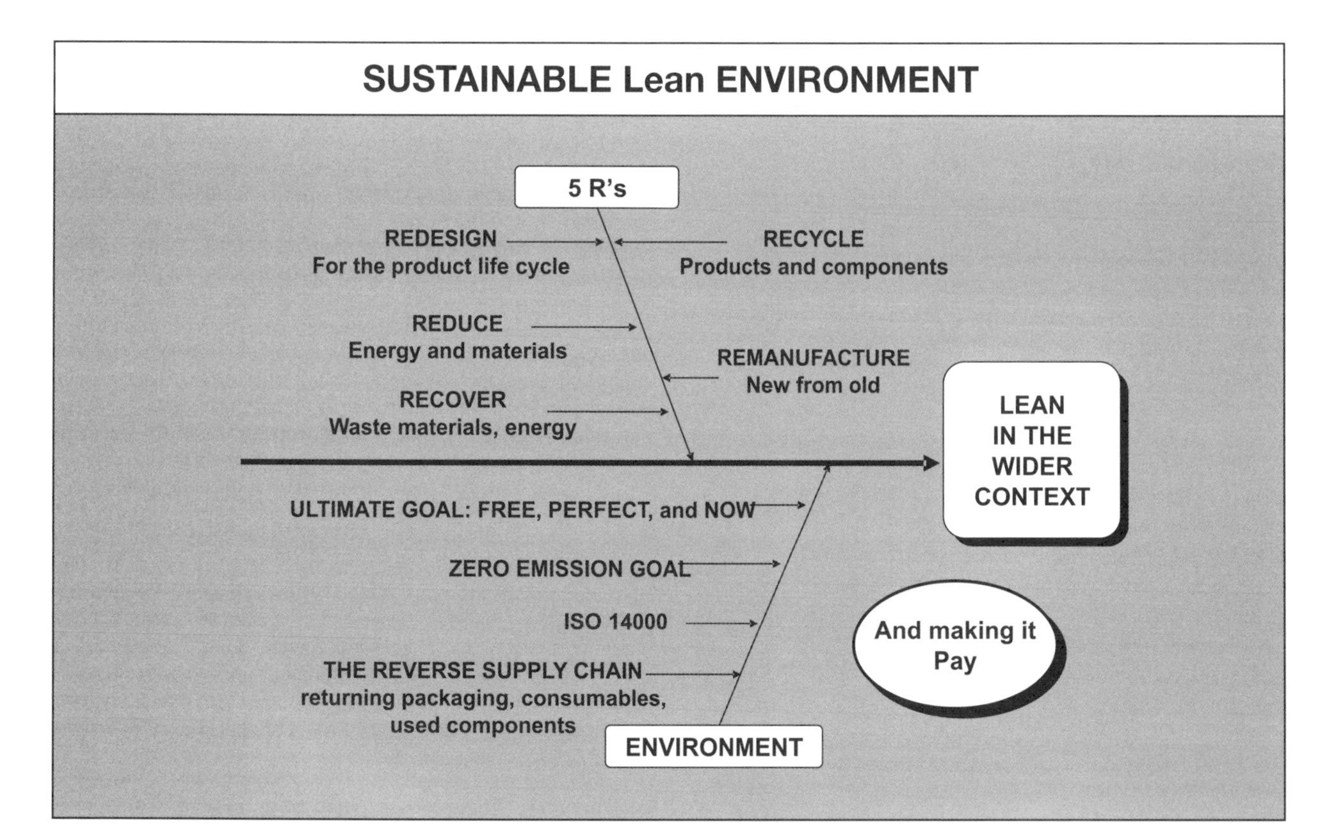
SUSTAINABLE Lean ENVIRONMENT
5 R's
REDESIGN
For the product life cycle
RECYCLE
Products and components
REDUCE
Energy and materials
REMANUFACTURE
New from old
RECOVER
Waste materials, energy
LEAN
IN THE
WIDER
CONTEXT
ULTIMATE GOAL: FREE, PERFECT, and NOW
ZERO EMISSION GOAL
ISO 14000
THE REVERSE SUPPLY CHAIN
returning packaging, consumables,
used components
ENVIRONMENT
And making it
Pay

Sustainable Lean Environment

Ultimate lean means sustainable lean. Ultimate lean means no waste in the "wider systems" of energy, materials, and pollution.

5R's

The book *Natural Capitalism* by Hawkins, Lovins and Lovins (Little, Brown, 2000) gives scores of exciting examples how products can profitably meet both environmental and performance objectives. Product design for the life cycle, including packaging during shipment, durability, ease of maintenance, ease of upgrading, the repair cycle, and ultimate disposal makes products more competitive. Customers, like good supplier partnership practice, are looking at total cost not just price. Likewise the reduction of energy and materials both during manufacture and in use makes for improved competitiveness. The recovery of waste materials during manufacture has long been promoted in good manufacturing companies. Perhaps less common is the recovery and use of packaging and energy conservation in the plant, the office, and in distribution. Similar remarks can be made for recycling. Recovery and recycling need to begin at the design stage whether for a product or for a factory. The former is more common, even trendy, but the latter is more unusual. Finally "re-man" is a growing trend with a lean manufacturing expertise of its own.

Environment

It is no news that environmental concerns are increasingly important. ISO14000 embodied these in a standard and several corporations have zero emission goals. More unusually engineering the reverse supply chain, where a company takes responsibility for the return of packaging, consumables and used components will surely grow. Make it pay.

The ultimate Lean is 'free, perfect, and now'. Impossible? Think Google, internet telephone calls, working from home, and the relentless march of products that cost less, consume less power, pollute less, last longer, are quieter. Can you leapfrog – now that you have the end in mind?

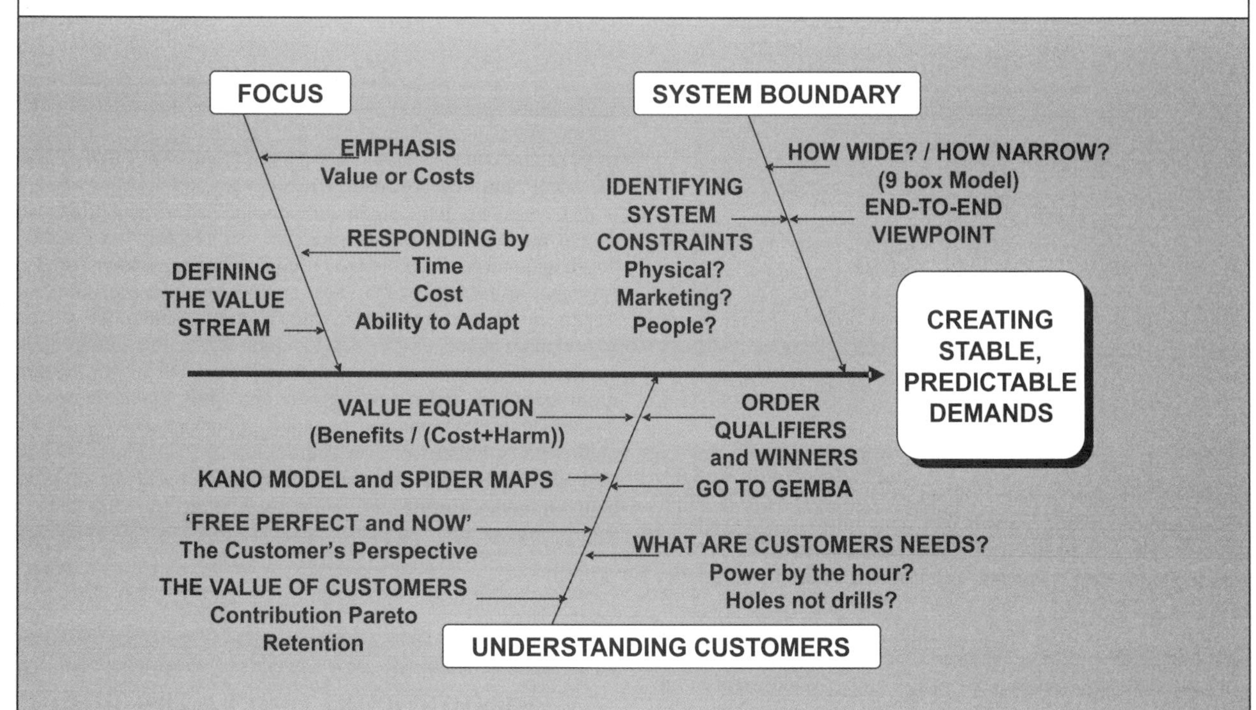
UNDERSTAND VALUE for Flow
FOCUS
EMPHASIS
Value or Costs
RESPONDING by
Time
Cost
Ability to Adapt
DEFINING
THE VALUE
STREAM
SYSTEM BOUNDARY
HOW WIDE? / HOW NARROW?
(9 box Model)
END-TO-END
VIEWPOINT
IDENTIFYING
SYSTEM
CONSTRAINTS
Physical?
Marketing?
People?
CREATING
STABLE,
PREDICTABLE
DEMANDS
VALUE EQUATION
(Benefits / (Cost+Harm))
ORDER
QUALIFIERS
and WINNERS
KANO MODEL and SPIDER MAPS
GO TO GEMBA
'FREE PERFECT and NOW'
The Customer's Perspective
WHAT ARE CUSTOMERS NEEDS?
Power by the hour?
Holes not drills?
THE VALUE OF CUSTOMERS
Contribution Pareto
Retention
UNDERSTANDING CUSTOMERS

UNDERSTAND VALUE for Flow

Value is Womack & Jones' first Lean principle.

Understanding Customers

This is complex, but often glossed over. Begin with the value equation – the aim being either to increase benefits or reduce costs or both. In the West today, the emphasis has swung towards benefits since many cannot compete on cost with China or India. There is also decreasing harm – to the environment, to employees and other stakeholders – it may be hard to win customers this way, but not impossible.

The Kano model is widely used. Every product or service has three types of characteristic. Basics must be met and are expected. Performance factors can cause disgust at one extreme, delight at the other. Delighters are not expected. The task is to identify and guarantee basics, improve the performance factors, and try to include low cost delighters. Another perspective is to distinguish 'order qualifiers' (must haves) from 'order winners' – and to compete accordingly.

The true needs of customers must be identified. 'Holes not drills', 'power by the hour' not a new jet engine. Truly to understand means being close to the customer – at Gemba – like Lexus sending a design team to live in California. And the ultimate customer requirement, but real challenge, is for 'free, perfect, and now'.

Whilst an important aim is to build and retain customers, not all customers are worth retaining. Some may conflict with priorities, some may be low value, some may be plain 'terrorists'.

System Boundary and Focus

Focus means building value streams that are specific to customer needs. The right balance between time, cost and flexibility – not blind movement of all manufacture to China. The complete picture must be known – what is the penalty for lead time, for responsiveness, for service? This may lead to some stable, common items being moved to low cost locations but retaining those where the order winner is responsiveness and lead time. Draw the system boundary appropriately – not necessarily to coincide with the factory walls.

The TRIZ 9 box model is a framework for sub-system, system and wider system along one axis, and for past, present and future along the other. Take a tree: an acorn or piece of wood; a branch or a forest; a piece of timber or a piece of coal. Which is appropriate?

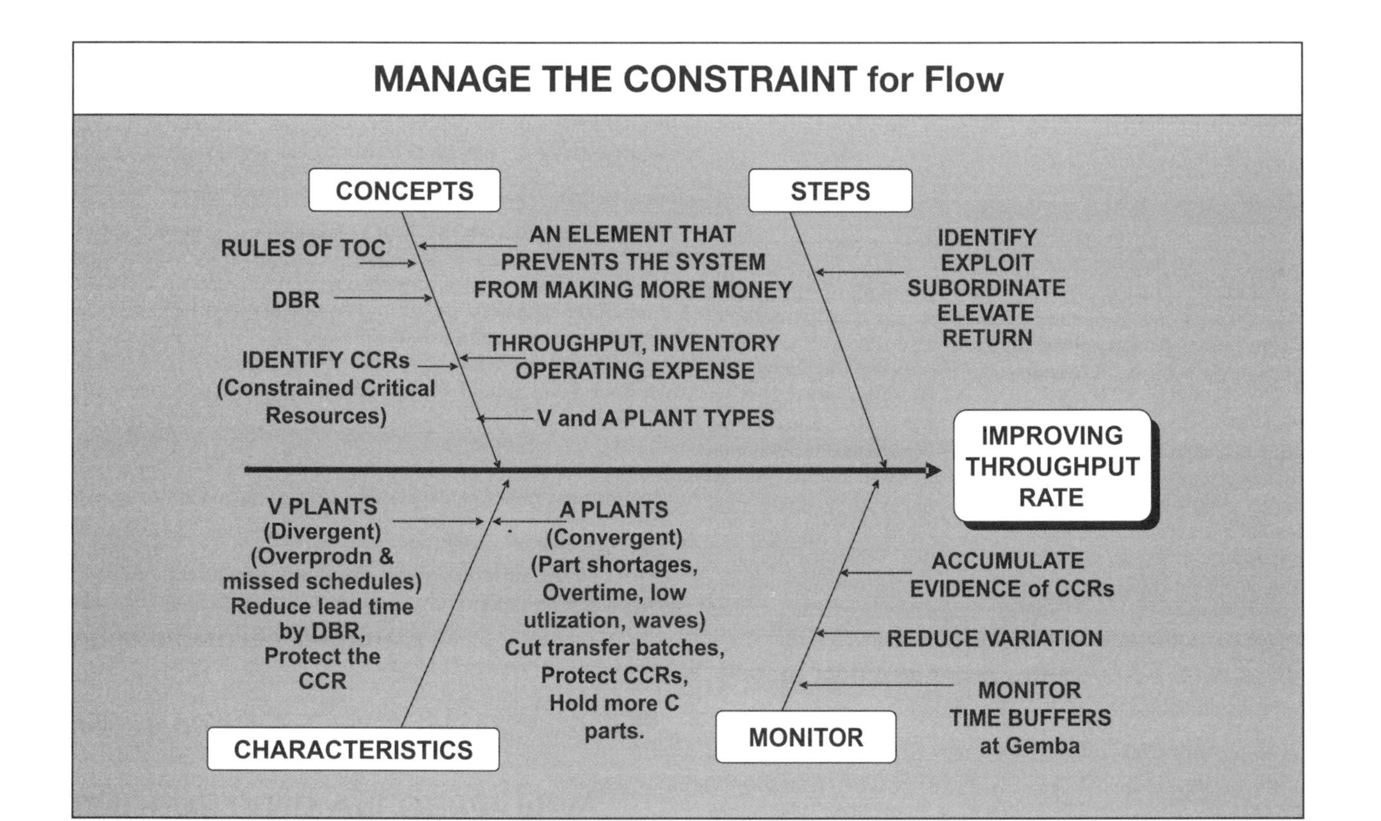
MANAGE THE CONSTRAINT for Flow
CONCEPTS
RULES OF TOC
DBR
IDENTIFY CCRs
(Constrained Critical
Resources)
AN ELEMENT THAT
PREVENTS THE SYSTEM
FROM MAKING MORE MONEY
THROUGHPUT, INVENTORY
OPERATING EXPENSE
V and A PLANT TYPES
STEPS
IDENTIFY
EXPLOIT
SUBORDINATE
ELEVATE
RETURN
IMPROVING
THROUGHPUT
RATE
CHARACTERISTICS
V PLANTS
(Divergent)
(Overprodn &
missed schedules)
Reduce lead time
by DBR,
Protect the
CCR
A PLANTS
(Convergent)
(Part shortages,
Overtime, low
utlization, waves)
Cut transfer batches,
Protect CCRs,
Hold more C
parts.
MONITOR
ACCUMULATE
EVIDENCE of CCRs
REDUCE VARIATION
MONITOR
TIME BUFFERS
at Gemba

MANAGE THE CONSTRAINT

Concepts

A constraint is something that prevents an enterprise from making more money – this may be physical, managerial, marketing, or human. A bottleneck is a restriction in physical capacity in a value stream. Understanding, identifying, and reducing both are vital for flow.

Steps

The steps of Goldratt's Theory of Constraints are powerful in any operation environment, including Lean. First, recognise the bottleneck. Then 'exploit' it – make sure that it keeps working; reduce changeover, wring every possible hour out of it. Then subordinate – ensure that flow to the bottleneck is uninterrupted and that it is protected by sufficient and the right inventory. Offload work that can be done on other machines. Only then 'elevate' – work extra shifts, buy an extra machine. Then return to the first step.

Characteristics

Goldratt's 10 synchronous principles are also most useful in many lean environments. Two famous ones are 'an hour lost at a bottleneck is an hour lost for the (value stream), and an hour lost at a non-bottleneck is merely a mirage.'

A 'constrained critical resource' (CCR) may sometimes be a bottleneck (over a short or long horizon), at other times not, sometimes severely overloaded, other times not. Are the root causes in demand, in job release, in batching, in schedule adherence?

DBR and CONWIP are most applicable where there are major bottlenecks and/or resources that are shared across more than one value stream.

DBR or Drum Buffer Rope is multi-stage pull. The drum is the bottleneck, the buffer is the timed quantity of inventory (hours of work waiting) that protects the bottleneck. The rope joins the bottleneck to the gateway work centre – what gets let out is let in. You can have a push system between the gateway and the bottleneck.

CONWIP (Constant work in progress) links the last process with the first. Whatever is let out is let in – so WIP is constant. This has significant advantages of ease of implementation, and inventory tending to accumulate just where it is needed – but is less focused than DBR.

Monitor

Sometimes bottlenecks and CCRs may not be obvious or may change. So several resources may have to be monitored to build the evidence. Monitor the buffer carefully, at Gemba, every day – not just in terms of quantity, but ensuring that the right products are there – not too early or late. Seek to reduce the time variation of jobs arriving late or early at the bottleneck. Monitor the usage of bottlenecks (OEE?). Hold the morning meeting at the bottleneck, not in the office.

PULL and SYNCHRONIZE for Flow

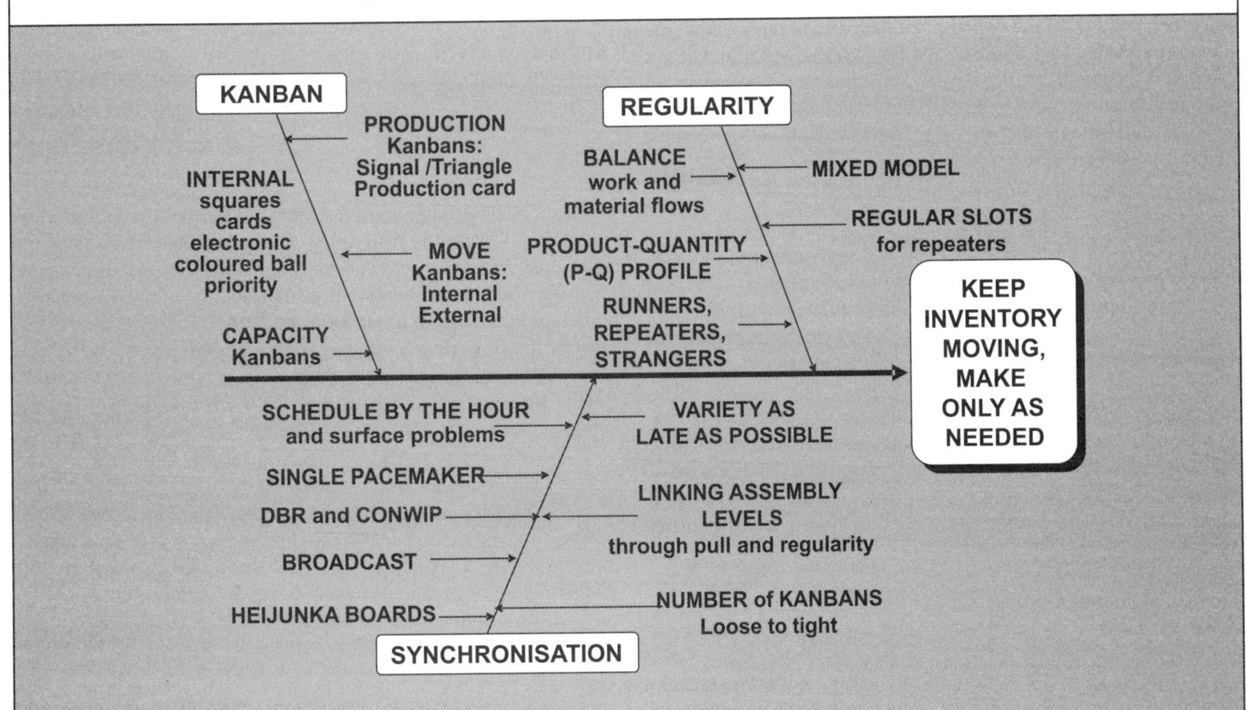
KANBAN
PRODUCTION Kanbans: Signal /Triangle Production card
INTERNAL squares cards electronic coloured ball priority
MOVE Kanbans: Internal External
CAPACITY Kanbans
REGULARITY
BALANCE work and material flows
MIXED MODEL
REGULAR SLOTS for repeaters
PRODUCT-QUANTITY (P-Q) PROFILE
RUNNERS, REPEATERS, STRANGERS
KEEP INVENTORY MOVING, MAKE ONLY AS NEEDED
SCHEDULE BY THE HOUR and surface problems
VARIETY AS LATE AS POSSIBLE
SINGLE PACEMAKER
LINKING ASSEMBLY LEVELS through pull and regularity
DBR and CONWIP
BROADCAST
HEIJUNKA BOARDS
NUMBER of KANBANS Loose to tight
SYNCHRONISATION

PULL and SYNCHRONIZE for Flow

Lean is about pull and flow – the third and fourth lean principles. The vision is that parts and products flow like a river whose volume matches the demand rate. Gradually, the flow erodes the loops and finds short cuts, so that lengths decrease and problem rocks are worn away. With time, dams and lakes along the route are made to disappear, so progress downstream is not delayed. Shortening the flow length means that flow can be even and does not have to be released early in anticipation of uncertain demand.

Kanban

Kanban is suitable for any type of repetitive manufacture, and variations may be suitable for non-repetitive. A kanban works between a pair of workstations only. Parts are pulled by the next workstation only as needed, and the supplier workstation stops work if no parts are pulled. This prevents overproduction and synchronises operations. Ideally only a single pacemaker process is scheduled, with all subassemblies and components being pulled in as needed.

There are two general types of kanban. The product type signals for an identical part or batch to be made at a workstation. A move or conveyance kanban is used by a material handler as the instruction to go fetch parts from a supermarket or feeding workstation. Kanban can work internally or externally. Internally, kanban squares are the most simple type: when empty, fill it; when full do not make more. Kanban cards may be single or dual. The far more common single card is a physical signal to make a replacement. No card, no make. Priority kanbans are simply pull cards but with colours to indicate urgency. Parts are pulled in order green, yellow, red but replenished in the reverse order. The batch made may be red only, or red and yellow, or red yellow and green. An alternative accumulates cards in a column or batch box until a trip point is reached signifying that production must commence. Dual card kanban has production cards and move cards and allows finer tuning and different move and make quantities. Electronic versions can be displayed. Externally, physical cards can be used but so too can faxban or e-ban.

A Heijunka (level production) board authorises production in pitch time intervals. The board is loaded up with the mix of products, and of course is visible.

The number of kanbans and parts in a loop depends upon stock-out risk, lead-time, part cost, and material handling. (Demand x total lead time)/container size. Normally, start "slack" and gradually tighten.

CONWIP and DBR (drum buffer rope) are multi-stage pull systems.

Synchronisation

The aim is to keep materials moving – keeping people and a machine moving is less important. But do not allow materials to move faster than customer demand – work at the takt time. Unfortunately seasonality and acquire-and-make lead times longer

than customer expectations are a fact of life. So while attacking lead times by all the techniques in this book, aim to add value as late as possible. Seek lower level commonality or platforms. This is why design is such a powerful weapon for better schedules. Forward visibility and rolling schedules aim to clarify expectations both internally and externally. Change as little as possible. Internally, the broadcast system is used in car plants and elsewhere where several assemblies need to synchronise. Broadcast launches each branch in exactly the right sequence.

Regularity aims at a (no surprises) schedule. In batch production, try to make the same products at about the same time every day or every week. This helps maintenance, changeovers, suppliers, tooling, and workforce. In assembly, aim for mixed model production: a repeating sequence of mixed products all day rather than A in morning, B in afternoon. This allows smooth, continuous flow.

Heijunka is a major concept. The heijunka board is located at the pacemaker. A heijunka board contains columns that are the pitch increment times spread evenly throughout the day. (Pitch = takt x container size). Rows are products. When loaded, each column contains a card authorizing production in that particular time slot. So work is spread evenly throughout the day. It is visible. If production slips, and the card cannot be completed, it is known immediately. A material handler may be the person who ensures regular flow, by beginning and ending each route every pitch increment. On route he picks up conveyance kanbans from workstations, picks from the supermarket, then delivers parts on his next round.

Schedule by the hour is an alternative. Each hour's work is planned and tracked. Not quite as visible and motivating as heijunka, but almost. Both 'surface' problems quickly.

ALIGN DEMAND for Flow

Lean works best when there is a uniform flow of products right along the chain. This will never be perfect, but the purpose of demand management is to make sure that flow is as regular as possible.

Stability

The aim is stability of schedules. There should be no incentives that create demand amplification. For instance, quantity discounts encourage the buying of unneeded quantities in the short term. Rather give discounts for regular orders. Forcing out inventory discourages accountants and others from playing games with inventory to massage the balance sheet. Marketing has an important role to play by encouraging demand when it is low and discouraging when it is high. Management should adopt practices that discourage the end of month "hockey stick". One possibility is to stagger end-of-month dates for salesmen. Forecasting by family and then breaking down the forecast into product groups discourages unrealistic demands.

Sales and operation planning teams encourage looking at demands from both aspects. Available-to-promise (ATP) logic gives a good indication to sales of the available capacity and encourages stability.

Types of Demand

Value Demand is first time demand. Failure demand (John Seddon's concept) stems from a failure to do something correctly or at all. Essential therefore to know how much of demand is failure demand that should be eliminated. Audit for this.

Base and flex capacity is increasingly relevant with low cost country manufacture. How much demand is 'base' – steady and predictable, where long lead times are acceptable; and 'flex' – variable, unpredictable, requiring short term response, with cost less of an issue. Different facilities, even different countries may be required for each.

And how variable is demand? Is it common cause variation, where inventory buffers can adequately protect, or special cause requiring more flexible facilities and patterns of working?

Supply Chain Amplification

This is where, at each stage along the supply or distribution chain, demand instability increases. The first step towards elimination is understanding. The causes of this so-called Bullwhip or Forrester effect are:

(a) the Burbidge effect that results from batching decisions that translate uniform demands into lumpy demands. These lumpy demands become ever more pronounced.

(b) Demand signal instability occurs when members of the chain read the signals or forecasts incorrectly and put in orders to the next stage to anticipate these false signals.

(c) Buying behaviour instability results from taking advantage of quantity discounts or in anticipation of price rises that cause false demand patterns.

ALIGN DEMAND for Flow

STABILITY

- **INCENTIVES** for regularity, not quantity
- **ROLE OF MARKETING** and dealers
- **ROLE OF MANAGEMENT** discourage hockey stick
- **FORECASTING** aggregate
- **UNDERSTANDING REQD LEAD TIMES** filling troughs,cutting peaks
- **SALES & OPERATION Planning**

TYPES OF DEMAND

- **VALUE and FAILURE Demand**
- **BASE and FLEX Capacity**
- **DEMAND VARIATION** Common & Special cause

SUPPLY CHAIN AMPLIFICATION

- **AWARENESS OF BULLWHIP**
  - Forrester Effect
  - Burbidge Batching
  - Demand Signal Processing
  - Buying Behaviour
  - Rationing and Gaming
- **AMPLIFICATION REDUCTION**
  - Reduce response time
  - Share information
  - Co-ordinate replenishment
  - Allocation policies
- **BUILD TO ORDER** Philosophy
- **QUICK RESPONSE** EPOS, Web chain linkages

CREATING STABLE, PREDICTABLE DEMANDS

(d) Rationing and gaming are policies adopted by suppliers for apparent short-term advantage. Rationing involves creating false shortages and gaming involves for instance building up inventory in anticipation of year-end. If suppliers know that demands are increasing and shortages likely they may exaggerate their orders.

Amplification reduction involves one or more of the following:

(a) A reduction in response time so those forecasts are more accurate or can be eliminated.
(b) Sharing information right along the chain enables true demands to be communicated. Uniform schedules can then be agreed.
(c) The co ordination of replenishment inventory prevents false demands from being communicated. All members of the chain should be made aware of ways in which replenishment systems operate so as to prevent false interpretation of demands.

Quick response and efficient consumer response, pioneered in the grocery and apparel industries, encourages direct links with electronic point of sale with demands communicated immediately along the chain. This is combined with design and distribution actions – see separate sections.

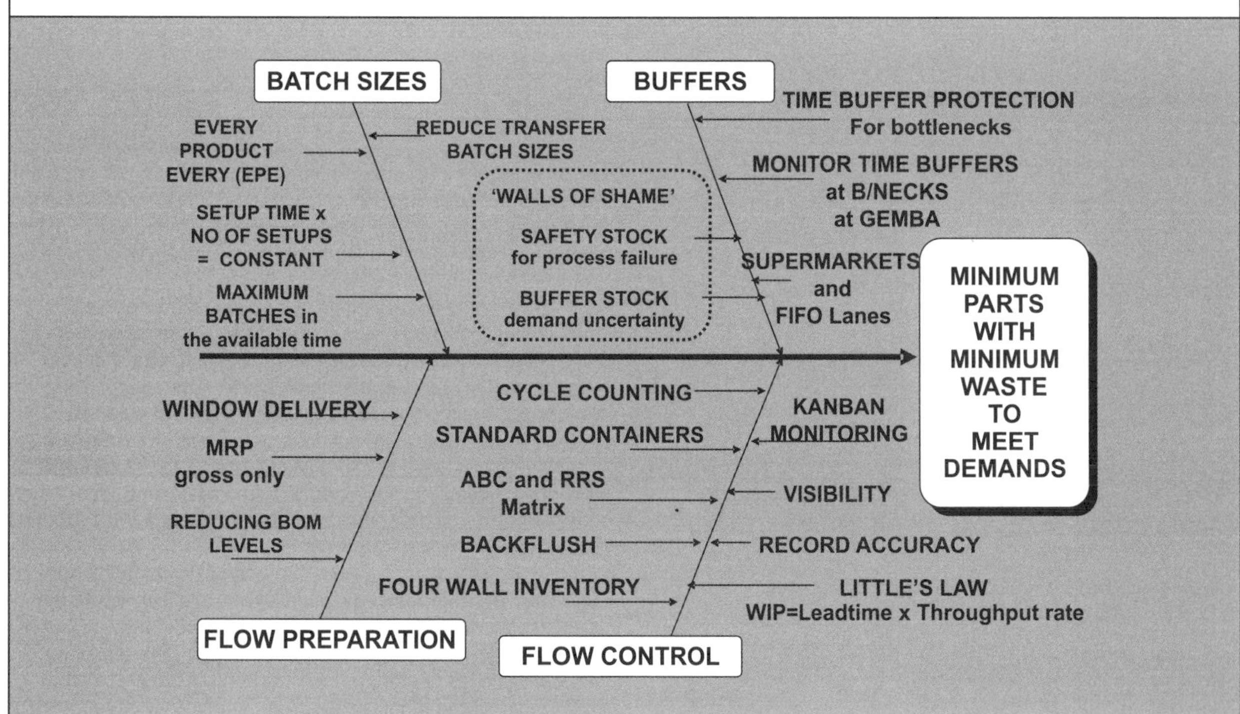
INVENTORY for Flow
BATCH SIZES
EVERY PRODUCT EVERY (EPE)
REDUCE TRANSFER BATCH SIZES
SETUP TIME x NO OF SETUPS = CONSTANT
MAXIMUM BATCHES in the available time
BUFFERS
TIME BUFFER PROTECTION For bottlenecks
MONITOR TIME BUFFERS at B/NECKS at GEMBA
'WALLS OF SHAME'
SAFETY STOCK for process failure
BUFFER STOCK demand uncertainty
SUPERMARKETS and FIFO Lanes
MINIMUM PARTS WITH MINIMUM WASTE TO MEET DEMANDS
WINDOW DELIVERY
MRP gross only
REDUCING BOM LEVELS
FLOW PREPARATION
CYCLE COUNTING
STANDARD CONTAINERS
ABC and RRS Matrix
BACKFLUSH
FOUR WALL INVENTORY
KANBAN MONITORING
VISIBILITY
RECORD ACCURACY
LITTLE'S LAW
WIP=Leadtime x Throughput rate
FLOW CONTROL

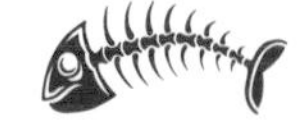

INVENTORY for Flow

Lean is not all about inventory reduction. But inventory reduction helps to move you towards lean by exposing problems, reducing lead-time, improving visibility and responsiveness to quality problems, and by reducing flow length. In fact, good inventory performance is the RESULT of other lean activities. Reducing inventory arbitrarily is often counterproductive.

Having an appropriate amount of inventory to ensure flow IS Lean. Inappropriate inventories that work against flow IS NOT Lean.

Batch Size

A key for flexibility is batch size reduction. It helps to establish a link with changeover time. As changeover time is reduced, the number of changeovers should increase so their product remains a constant. If changeover time is halved, number of changeovers should double and batch size should halve. Note that this does not correspond with EOQ thinking! Use the EPE principle – making use of all available time to do changeovers and hence to drive down batch size. Transfer batch sizes should be kept as small as possible compatible with (human-movable?) material handling – so as to maximise overlap and flow.

Buffers

A finished goods buffer is a 'wall of shame' – but better to have some to ensure flow. This does not mean excessive inventories.

Buffer inventory protects against uncertain demand. Safety inventory protects against internal disruption due to breakdowns, quality problems and the like.

A supermarket is an area where inventory is collected together (as opposed to scattered everywhere), where the material handler or runner 'goes shopping' with kanban cards, often on a regular route. A FIFO (first in first out) lane is an in-process inventory store with a maximum length, with FIFO discipline and ideally no double handling. This may mean two lanes.

Time Buffers protect bottlenecks and should be monitored at the bottleneck. Awareness of the reasons for buffers – maintenance, quality, supply variability, lead times – should lead to immediate cuts in buffers when reasons are removed through improvement efforts.

With schedule stability (heijunka?) and adherence, a virtuous circle can happen. The feedback loop works like this: cutting lead times (as a result of various lean activities) improves schedule adherence. With improved adherence buffers can be cut. And cutting buffers leads to a cut in lead-time. And so on. But for finished goods the situation may be different: with many smaller batch sizes instead of a fewer larger batches, there will be more occasions during which there is a risk of stock-out. This means that it may be necessary to increase safety stocks – but remember that lead times are down so this should compensate. And overall WIP levels will be sharply down. As Lean progresses it may be possible to convert make-to-stock operations to make to order, resulting in better service with lower inventory.

Flow Control

Little's law is fundamental. WIP = lead-time x throughput rate. So there are two routes to reduce WIP. But also throughput cannot be increased without either increasing WIP or reducing lead-time. This is sometimes forgotten!

Record accuracy and bill of material accuracy is also fundamental. The former can be improved by cycle counting, counting a few parts each day and tracking sources of error. However, in lean, count by frequency of use not part value. Standardised containers or "eggcrates" containing specific numbers of parts make counting easier. And visibility is improved by kanban.

For supply and distribution inventories, ABC (80/20) analysis is highly cost effective – paying particular attention to A category parts, and simply having C parts. In manufacture, A parts are brought to the line under kanban control, C parts are replenished by two bin methods. Throughout, all storage locations should be designed on the visibility and footprinting principle – making deviations immediately apparent. SPC principles can be used to control and improve record accuracy and to monitor supply lead times. Monitor delivery performance on time, quantity, and quality – failure on any one represents overall failure.

Tracking inventory is waste, particularly when fast moving. So record it only when it enters and leaves – the "four wall" system. With low defect levels, backflushing becomes possible – moving from subassembly backflushing to product level superflush. Flushing updates inventory records by deducting all parts that are assumed to have been used. Backflushing also gives a check on bill of material accuracy.

Kanban monitoring keeps visible track of backlogs by the number of cards on the board. Externally, kanban monitoring helps keep track of the sequence of arrival and departure of cards.

See the Essential Paretos.

Flow Preparation

Flow preparation begins with good accuracy, as above. MRP may be required but only for planning purposes, not execution. Gross-only MRP (no netting) may suffice at well developed lean sites. Reducing bill of material levels does away with unnecessary complexity. Single level bills are the norm in cellular manufacturing. BOMs should be restructured in line with changes in layout. Window deliveries, targeted at specific times, extend flow preparation to the supply chain.

Note that MRP does not work for shop floor execution because it makes the fatal error of not recognising variation. It is also less visible, and has too long a response cycle. Batch and queue thinking is inherent.

COMPRESS LEAD TIME for Flow

Time-based competitiveness is fundamental to Lean. As Ohno said, 'All we are trying to do is to reduce the time from order to cash', not just the manufacturing lead time.

Schedule

Scheduling plays the key role. A single pacemaker coordinates the value stream, preventing unnecessary accumulation of inventory and avoiding amplification. The pacemaker may be a heijunka board, a schedule by the hour, a DBR system, or a CONWIP system, the last two where there are strong bottlenecks or shared resources. EPE (every product every) regularity may be built into these systems so that this week looks as much like last week as possible and so that there is a regular repeating sequence where changeovers are involved.

Buffers contribute. Upstream don't be afraid of having buffers to ensure against delivery and supply quality failures until things are sorted out. Downstream, buffer against uncertain demand. But between these buffers there should be continuous flow and minimal inventories. The reduction of WIP inventories can easily compensate for increases upstream and downstream.

Capacity

Queuing Theory teaches that to plan for full capacity courts disaster and long lead times because of variation. And variation is impossible to eliminate. So a degree of 'undercapacity scheduling' is highly desirable. The load and capacity situation at constrained resources must be calculated and monitored. Where load creeps up beyond say 85% of capacity – beware! But capacity can also be influenced by flexibility of hours, people, and maybe machines.

Inventory

Reduction of WIP inventories, reduction of batch sizes and reduction of transfer (move) quantities all reduce lead time. So each must be actively managed. When changeover is reduced, this must be translated into batch size reduction, and so on.

The RRS/RRR, runners, repeaters, strangers/rogues, idea means that

- runners should enjoy dedicated facilities; note that profit not volume may lead to dedicated facilities,
- repeaters should enjoy regular slots in the schedule: same time each day or week; even better run them on a mixed model heijunka sequence
- strangers can be handled by periodic runs or postponement inventories.

One piece flow or as close to this as possible, perhaps one container at a time, reduces leadtime but also uncovers quality problems and reduces risk.

Muda, Muri, Mura

Waste, overburden and unevenness are the enemy. All are addressed by kaizen events, by awareness of ergonomics and workplace conditions, and flow systems like heijunka. Engineering changes should be grouped so as to minimise disruption.

COMPRESS LEAD TIME for Flow

SCHEDULE

- DBR and CONWIP PRINCIPLES
- UNDERCAPACITY SCHEDULING
- LEAD TIME VARIATION GAP
- HEIJUNKA or BY THE HOUR Control
- EPE REGULARITY
- SINGLE PACEMAKER Concept
- ALLOWING UNINTERUPTED FLOW
  - Upstream: quality buffers
  - Downstream: demand buffers
  - but overall reduced leadtime
- SCHEDULE STABILITY time fences, plateaus

CAPACITY

- PROVIDING ADEQUATE CAPACITY
- LOAD CALCULATIONS on heavily loaded and, convergent resources
- CAPACITY FROM FLEXIBILITY job and hours

RELENTLESS REDUCTION In LEAD TIME

INVENTORY

- POSTPONEMENT rolling firming
- REMOVAL OF INVENTORY
- BUFFER Protection At bottlenecks and convergencies only
- TRANSFER QUANTITY REDUCTION, and container size
- ALLOWING ONE PIECE FLOW
- BATCH SIZE REDUCTION
- RUNNERS, REPEATERS, STRANGERS

WASTE

- ENGINEERING CHANGES grouped
- SUPPORTING MEASURES
- KAIZEN EVENTS
- LAYOUT and SPAGHETTI and CELLS
- MAPPING and TIME LINES

Pipeline Flow

The idea is to have flow, without the waste of warehousing. Cross docking shifts products from one truck to several delivery vehicles, so that inventory is warehoused for hours not days or weeks. Flow is aided by selecting appropriate channels, perhaps one for large customers, another for fast moving, a third for small customers. Flow may be aided by postponement in product, assembling at the last moment, or packaging, by customer type or language. A general principle is investment in flexibility rather than inventory, for instance in changeover, in transport, in capacity.

See the note on lead time variation gap under Transformation Fishbone.

Inventory

The ideal is to supply no-more and no-less, working under pull not push. This can only be achieved by a long-term end-to-end effort along the chain in the adoption of lean techniques and principles. Forcing lean by insisting on minimal buffers prevents game playing and amplification effects, and encourages the chain to work at the customer's rate. Where warehousing is necessary "Risk Pooling" whereby local warehouse inventory is centralised and local warehouses closed, results in less inventory. Although inventory reduction takes place the penalty may be in response time. However, inventory and other flexibility savings may mean that more costly quick distribution still pays.

Stockpoint packaging tries to minimise the costs of stacking shelves and material handling by packing product in final display form, perhaps on roller pallets.

Information

Is key. Quick Response linkages with EPOS terminals or internet allow true customer demands to be communicated. B2B e-business is uncovering huge opportunity for speed and waste reduction. Related is schedule visibility, schedule stability and removal of the "bullwhip" effect, which can also lead to huge savings. See the separate section on demand management. An associated step is to map the supply or distribution chain, particularly to identify wastes and the point where Push meets Pull, and how it can be made to move upstream in future. The "co-opetition" concept allows competitors to co-operate for mutual benefit against outsiders but still to compete. Examples are common standards, trains vs. airlines, national distribution vs. international competition. Preparation for order receipt is a form of changeover reduction in distribution whereby maximum preparation for both physical and information flows is made in advance of receipt. Examples are customs pre-clearance and synchronised operations with fruit picking. Key account management extends the supplier partnership concepts to key customers. Both sides win.

Scheduling software, decision support (DSS), and advanced production scheduling (APS) is generally not favoured in lean manufacturing, except sometimes for planning, but in distribution it certainly has a place to optimise warehouse location, inventory management, and cross docking.

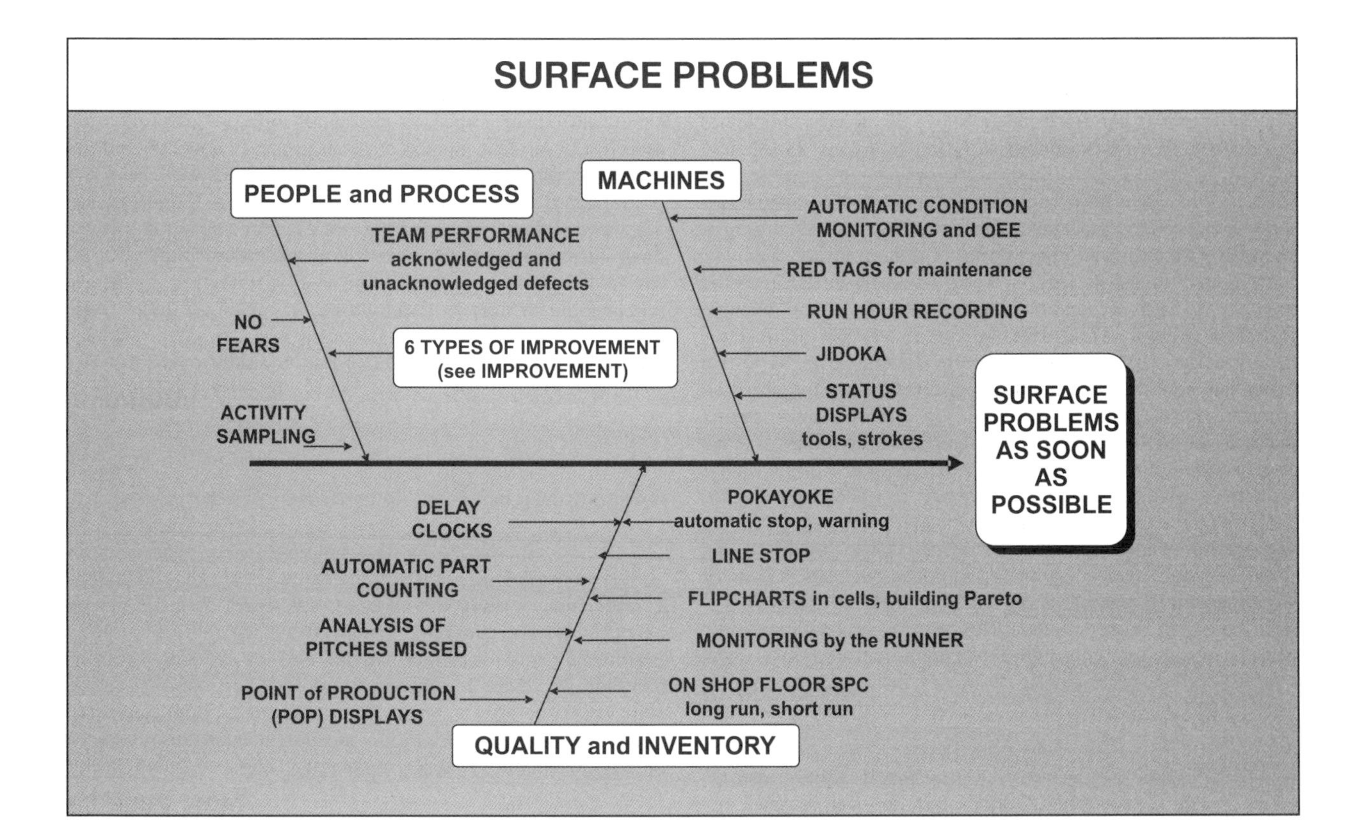
SURFACE PROBLEMS
PEOPLE and PROCESS
TEAM PERFORMANCE acknowledged and unacknowledged defects
NO FEARS
6 TYPES OF IMPROVEMENT (see IMPROVEMENT)
ACTIVITY SAMPLING
MACHINES
AUTOMATIC CONDITION MONITORING and OEE
RED TAGS for maintenance
RUN HOUR RECORDING
JIDOKA
STATUS DISPLAYS tools, strokes
SURFACE PROBLEMS AS SOON AS POSSIBLE
DELAY CLOCKS
POKAYOKE automatic stop, warning
LINE STOP
AUTOMATIC PART COUNTING
FLIPCHARTS in cells, building Pareto
ANALYSIS OF PITCHES MISSED
MONITORING by the RUNNER
POINT of PRODUCTION (POP) DISPLAYS
ON SHOP FLOOR SPC long run, short run
QUALITY and INVENTORY

SURFACE PROBLEMS

Improvement is the lean way of life. And rapid improvement can only be achieved through full participation.

One view of lean is that it is a system to expose problems and to solve them as soon as possible.

Later sections – surface problems, improve, improvement categories, seven wastes, service wastes, and kaizen events all deal with problems and improvement.

People and Process

The starting point is a 'no fears' culture – problems are to be welcomed; their resolution applauded. 'Drive out Fear' said Deming 40 years ago. A problem is an opportunity – management must give wholehearted support to this concept. Teams must not be afraid or penalised in discovering defects – in fact they should be rewarded. And acknowledgement is the first step to improvement – like a sport coach to whom weaknesses are explained so they can be resolved not hidden away.

Activity sampling – taking perhaps 200 to 300 random observations is a quick way of establishing the facts on time and activity utilisation but should never be done in secret. The best people to do this are operators, or office workers, themselves.

The six types of improvement are detailed on another figure. All are necessary.

Machines

OEE and automatic monitoring of downtime provide the essential data. Better is to be there when the problem occurs so that you know exactly what has happened. Both together is best. Red Tags highlight machine problems and display the urgency to maintenance crews. Some machines can display the number of strokes or hours since the last routine maintenance. And 'Jidoka' or failsafe builds in automatic devices that warn about or shut down a machine if things do wrong.

Quality and Inventory

Ways to surface problems include delay clocks that accumulate the total time a process has been stopped, a sign that highlights how many heijunka pitches have been missed today (black for one or two, then yellow, then red), POP (point of production) displays monitor the status, SPC charts show out-of-control conditions (these should be plotted and interpreted by operators), a flipchart on which operators accumulate a pareto record of problem types (rather than recording, say, the number of late shipments, better is to record the reasons why), and the runner who records problems on his circuit. Line stop that gives operators the authority to stop production when quality, shortage, or maintenance problems arise. Line stop must be accompanied by a signalling device to demand appropriate response. Line stoppage must attempt to seek the root cause, not merely arrange a temporary fix. Toyota lines stop many times each day – don't pass on a defect; fix it immediately.

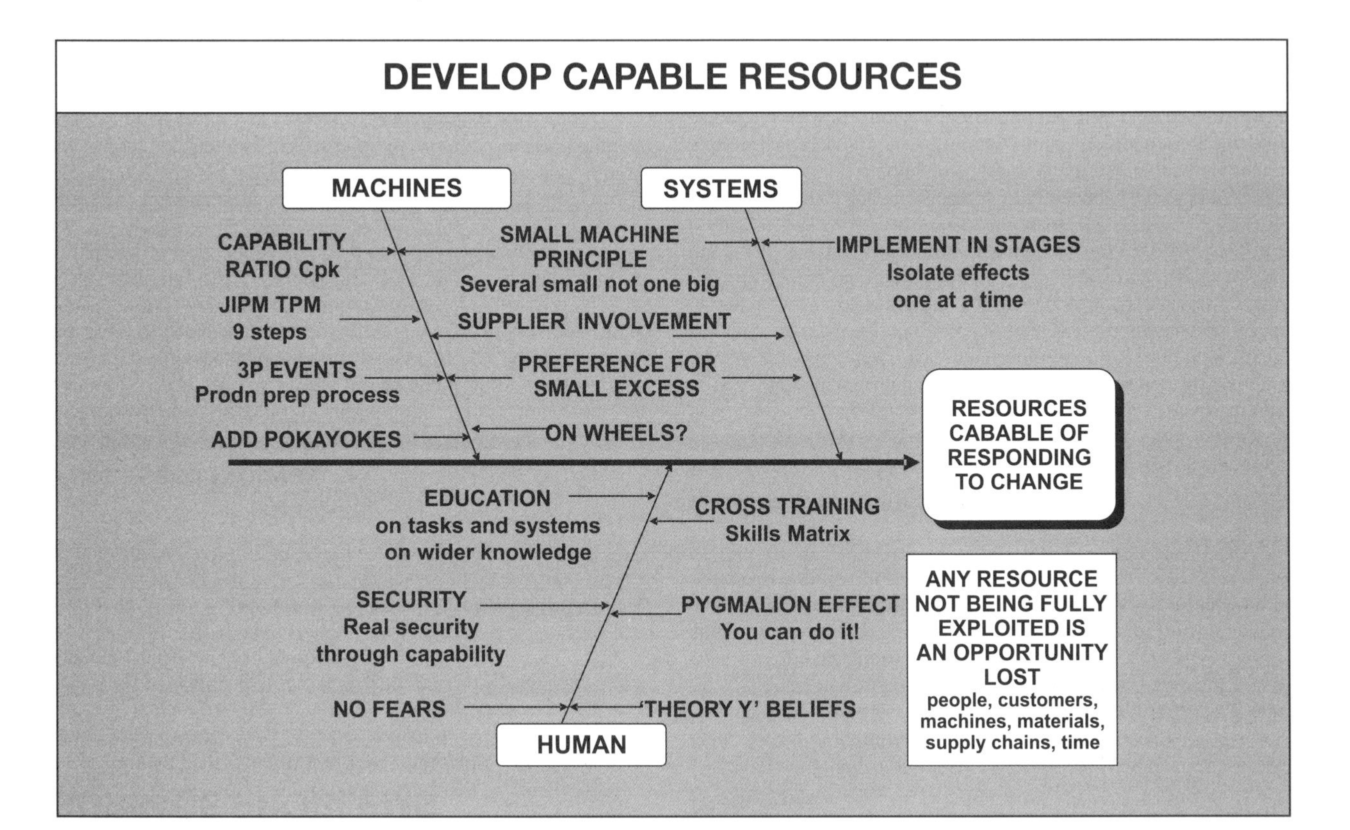
DEVELOP CAPABLE RESOURCES
MACHINES
SYSTEMS
CAPABILITY
RATIO Cpk
SMALL MACHINE
PRINCIPLE
Several small not one big
IMPLEMENT IN STAGES
Isolate effects
one at a time
JIPM TPM
9 steps
SUPPLIER INVOLVEMENT
3P EVENTS
Prodn prep process
PREFERENCE FOR
SMALL EXCESS
ADD POKAYOKES
ON WHEELS?
RESOURCES
CABABLE OF
RESPONDING
TO CHANGE
EDUCATION
on tasks and systems
on wider knowledge
CROSS TRAINING
Skills Matrix
SECURITY
Real security
through capability
PYGMALION EFFECT
You can do it!
NO FEARS
'THEORY Y' BELIEFS
HUMAN
ANY RESOURCE
NOT BEING FULLY
EXPLOITED IS
AN OPPORTUNITY
LOST
people, customers,
machines, materials,
supply chains, time

DEVELOP CAPABLE RESOURCES for Flow

Lean relies on capable resources: human, machine and information. These must be created, grown, absorbed, not 'implemented.'

The TRIZ idea that any resource not being fully exploited is an opportunity lost is useful. We have heard the expression used with operators 'bring your brain to work' (although sadly with some companies this is little more than woffle), but how about using the brains of customers (can we learn more about their true needs?), developing machines (can they be made more capable or flexible?), exploiting materials (what properties are not being used?), and developing the potential of supply chains (how can they be linked, integrated, speeded – like Zara).

Human

Peter Wickens, ex HR director of Nissan says "it's not a greenfield site that counts, it's a greenfield mind". Growing people begins with security, and no fears, progresses through beliefs like 'theory Y' and sees the potential in everyone – the Pygmalion effect. Education for the workforce, of course, is needed, not just on the immediate work, but on the whole value stream. So too is the education of customers on what the process is capable of delivering and the consequence for the supply chain and prices of placing erratic orders. You want everyone in the value stream identified with and by their particular customers.

Machines

Machine capability (Cpk) needs to be improved. The JIPM TPM method gets operators to strip down machines, sketch the parts, understand the workings, and then to develop appropriate procedures. Develop deep understanding. Critical parts are identified. Pokayokes are added. Wheels are added if feasible.

The 'best of the best' concept is useful whereby the best demonstrated performance of several like machines is combined to set the benchmark for all machines.

Machine suppliers need to be involved as soon as possible, fostering two-way communication like part supplier partners.

See also the small machines.

Systems

Implement in stages according to need, not 'big bang'. Test and validate. Use the 3P process. (See layout fishbone.) Remember anyone can catch you if your sole lead is in off-the-shelf systems and machines.

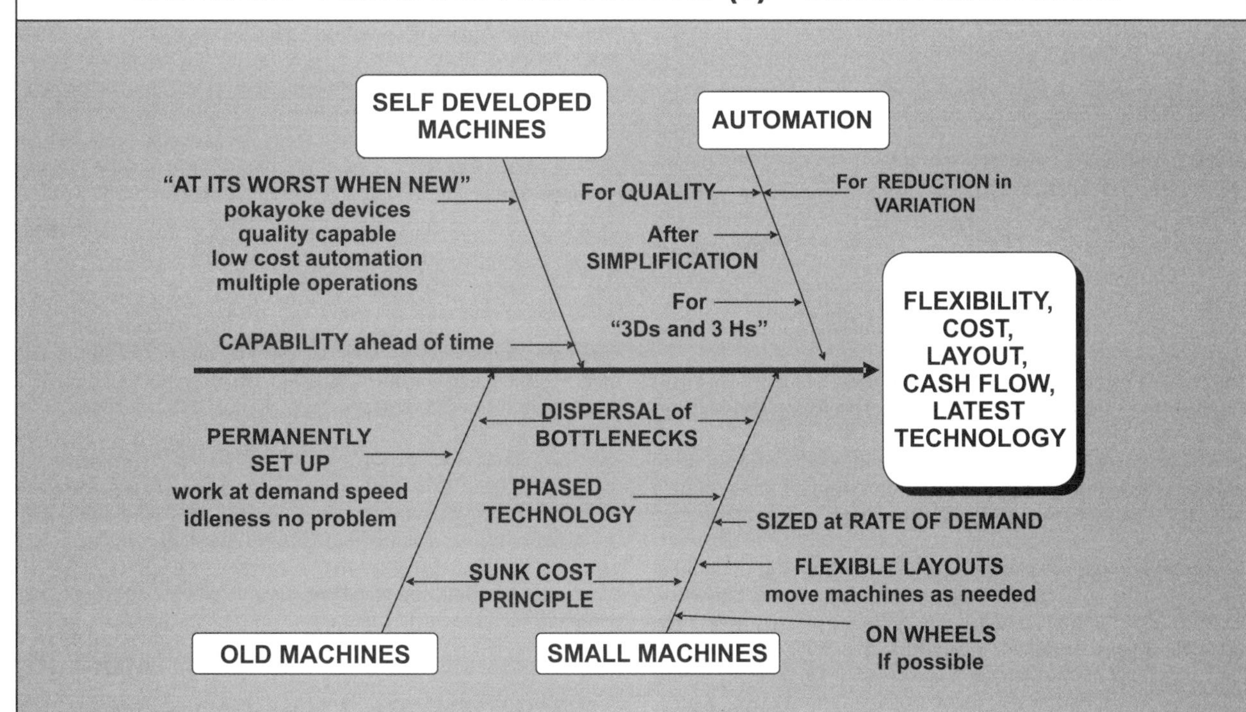
DEVELOP FLEXIBLE PROCESSES (1) - SMALL MACHINES
SELF DEVELOPED MACHINES
"AT ITS WORST WHEN NEW"
pokayoke devices
quality capable
low cost automation
multiple operations
CAPABILITY ahead of time
AUTOMATION
For QUALITY
For REDUCTION in VARIATION
After SIMPLIFICATION
For "3Ds and 3 Hs"
FLEXIBILITY, COST, LAYOUT, CASH FLOW, LATEST TECHNOLOGY
OLD MACHINES
PERMANENTLY SET UP
work at demand speed
idleness no problem
DISPERSAL of BOTTLENECKS
PHASED TECHNOLOGY
SUNK COST PRINCIPLE
SMALL MACHINES
SIZED at RATE OF DEMAND
FLEXIBLE LAYOUTS
move machines as needed
ON WHEELS
If possible

DEVELOP FLEXIBLE PROCESSES (1) – SMALL MACHINES

The SMALL MACHINE concept is one of the least recognised lean facilitators. The general principle is to use the smallest machine possible consistent with quality requirements. Several smaller machines instead of one bigger, faster one allows flexibility in layouts, easier scheduling, reduction in material handling, less vulnerability to breakdown, less vulnerability to bottleneck problems, possibly reduced cost through a mix of capability and through phasing of machine acquisition, improved cash flow and more frequent technology updates.

The related sunk cost principle means that the priority should be with minimising present and future costs, not with keeping machines working to "pay off" a cost which has already been incurred. Therefore utilisation is irrelevant unless it is a capacity constrained machine.

In fact, maximising utilisation is counterproductive, something we learn from statistical thinking and from highway congestion where progress stalls when utilisation gets too high. The reduction in variation in machine cycles is as important as cycle time itself.

Old Machines

The small machine concept can be extended to older machines. The best machine may well be an old machine that is quality capable, that is permanently set up, located just where needed, and that is written off in the books so that no-one cares about utilisation. It is throughput and lead-time that count. Beware of scrapping old machines that are still quality capable for machines that are faster.

Self Developed Machines

Why should a machine be "at its worst when new"? Because it may not yet have had pokayoke devices fitted, may not yet be quality capable, may not yet have had low cost automation devices integrated with it, and may not yet have been developed for multiple operations. And especially if variation has not been tackled.

Developing machine capabilities "ahead of the game" is good policy. You may not have the time when you need it.

Automation

The prime reason for automation in lean is for quality. The principle is not to automate waste. So simplify first. Ask whether a low cost solution is possible, a gravity feed rather than a robot. Good reasons for automation are dull, dirty, dangerous and hot, heavy, hazardous. Another good reason is reduction in variation. A bad reason is to reduce people. Machines don't make improvement suggestions.

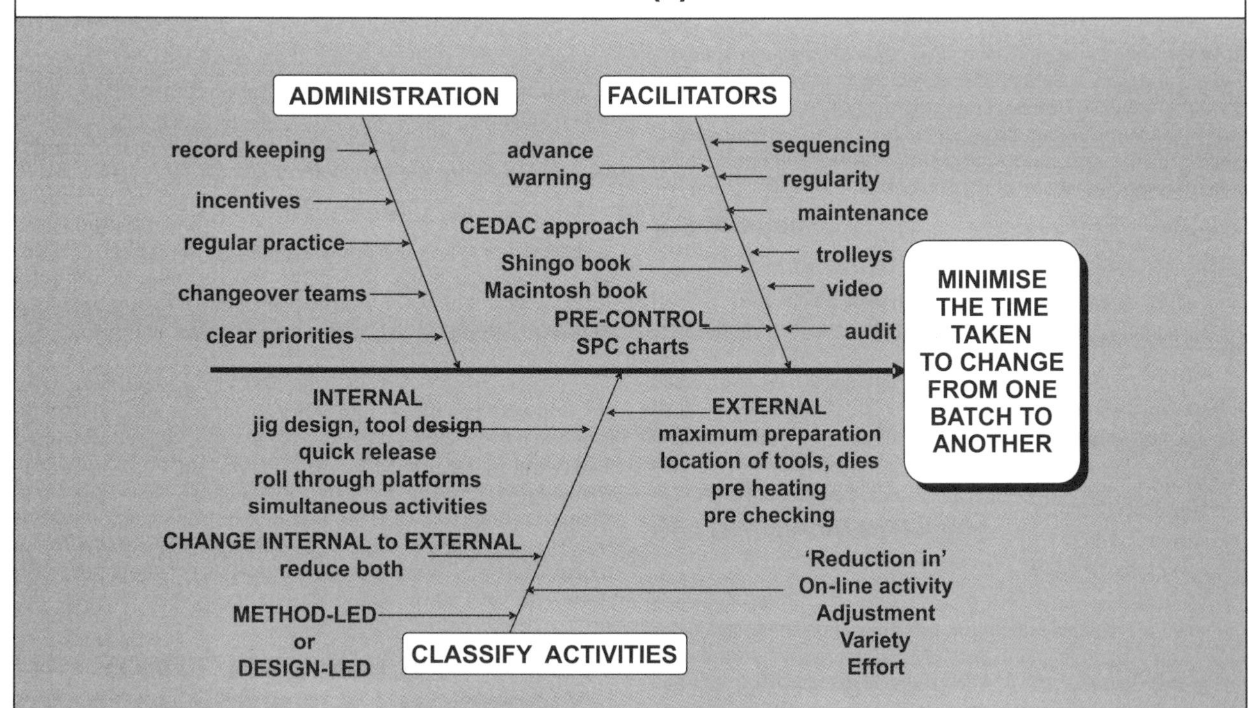
DEVELOP FLEXIBLE PROCESSES (2) - CHANGEOVER REDUCTION
ADMINISTRATION
record keeping
incentives
regular practice
changeover teams
clear priorities
FACILITATORS
advance warning
CEDAC approach
Shingo book
Macintosh book
PRE-CONTROL
SPC charts
sequencing
regularity
maintenance
trolleys
video
audit
MINIMISE THE TIME TAKEN TO CHANGE FROM ONE BATCH TO ANOTHER
INTERNAL
jig design, tool design
quick release
roll through platforms
simultaneous activities
CHANGE INTERNAL to EXTERNAL
reduce both
METHOD-LED
or
DESIGN-LED
CLASSIFY ACTIVITIES
EXTERNAL
maximum preparation
location of tools, dies
pre heating
pre checking
'Reduction in'
On-line activity
Adjustment
Variety
Effort

DEVELOP FLEXIBLE PROCESSES (2): CHANGEOVER REDUCTION

The prime reason for changeover reduction in lean is for flexibility and reduced batch sizes, leading to lead time competitiveness. Improved changeover also, surprisingly, leads to improved quality through consistent repetition. A less good reason is to increase capacity, especially if it leads to overproduction.

Note that changeover is usually defined as the time from the last piece of one batch to the first good piece of the next batch. Sometimes it is better to define it from full speed on last to full speed on next. Where batches are very small the limitation is not the internal changeover time when the machine is stopped, but the external time for changeover preparation. So both need to be reduced as well as the time for adjustment and inspection.

Note also that changeover reduction is not limited to machine changeover. Line changeover, vehicle load and unload, maintenance operations, and many office operations are also relevant.

Consistency is a big issue. It is not much good having a changeover that sometimes takes 10 minutes but sometimes takes 30 minutes. Often, to achieve schedule adherence, it is more important to be consistent than quick but variable. Standardisation should certainly be a goal.

The classic analogy is with a grand prix pit stop. The same principles apply.

Classify Activities

Shingo's classic single-minute exchange of die (SMED) approach is to flowchart the changeover and to classify into internal and external activities. See if any internal activities can be done externally. External: do the maximum amount of preparation before the machine is stopped. This includes locating tools and dies on trolleys, colour coding to avoid confusion, locating frequently used dies nearer to machines, pre-heating and pre-checking (and post changeover checking also to maximise the time available). Internal: many internal improvements involve the use of simple though sometimes sophisticated devices: quick release nuts, standard die heights, roll through platforms, jig and tool design, use of hydraulic and electric aids. Remember the quality side: incorporate failsafeing devices, off line checks, and testing procedures. Sometimes it is sampling that takes the longest time.

The process should be mapped and the "critical path" determined. A spaghetti diagram of operator movements is useful.

Macintosh at Bath University makes a plea for more 'design led' changeover attention, where quick changeover is designed in, rather than the 'method-led' approach of Shingo.

Facilitators

Correct sequencing of changeovers, from major to minor, from dark colour to light may help. So may regularity where a changeover takes place at approximately the same time each day or week. Dies are always ready, so is the forklift, so are the parts

to be processed, etc. Preventive maintenance of tools, dies, and machines is essential to retain changeover consistency. Trolleys on which all necessary tools and dies are placed, by shadowboard and colour coded, preferably at the correct height, are useful. Every changeover should be videoed with time lapse camera.

Advance warning means having a clear signal (lights, audio) when a changeover is due, to warn the changeover team and the forklift driver. Cause and Effect diagrams with addition of cards (CEDAC) can be used to record past achievements and tasks still to be done. Shingo's SMED book is the bible on changeover. But a more recent bible is Mackintosh's book.

Administration

An aspect frequently ignored is to chart every changeover time on a run diagram. This helps to encourage consistency and to trace sources of problems. Team members should feel free to write ideas and memos on the chart – use rather than appearance is preferred. Incentives are both financial and non-financial. Although output incentives are not compatible with lean, consistency and achievement may well be rewarded. Non-financial reward and recognition is necessary to retain good performance. As in a grand prix team, practise makes perfect; you don't have to make parts to practise and perfect a changeover. Teams, as in a grand prix, should do critical changeovers. And changeovers should enjoy clear priority over all (?) support activities; never delay a changeover by a non-customer-critical activity.

Lean and SIX SIGMA

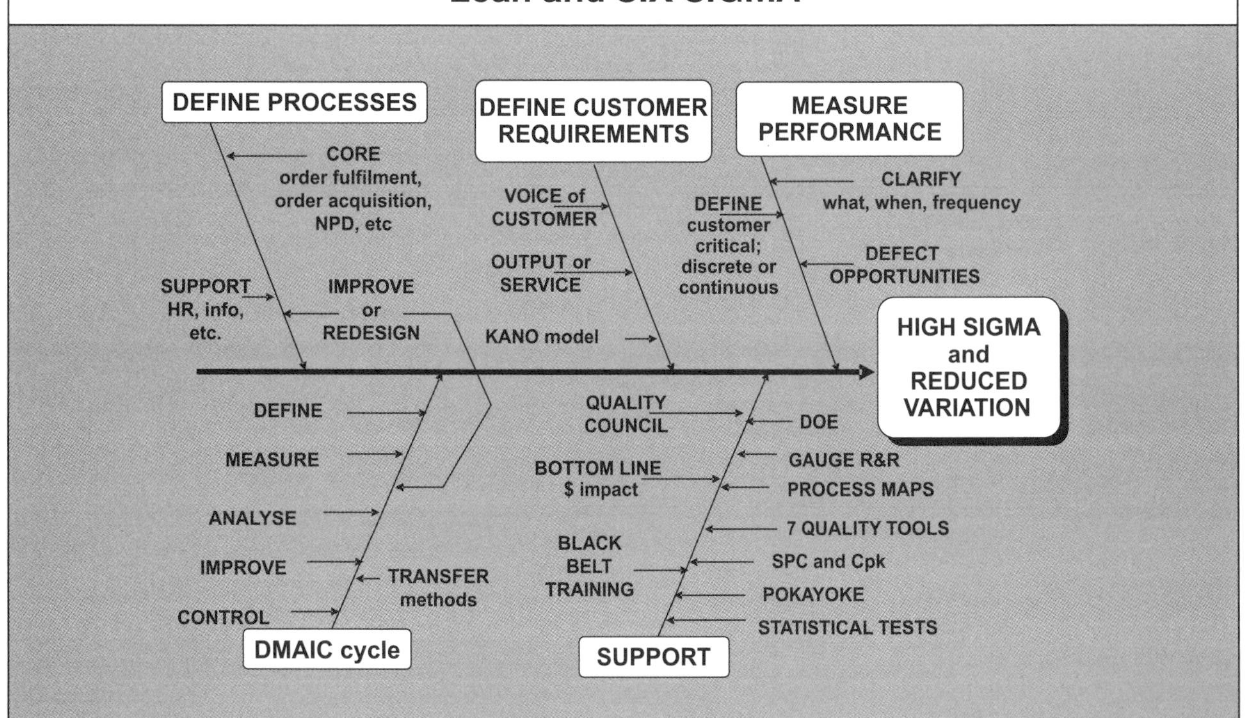

Lean and SIX SIGMA

Six Sigma is about process improvement and goes far beyond product defect rates. It is an ordered, tested methodology for widescale improvement in service and manufacture. Ultimately six sigma is not about quality improvement, it is about improving the bottom line.

DEFINE PROCESSES. The starting point. There are two types of process, "core" and "support" and two approaches "improvement" and "redesign". Core processes enjoy first priority. Note "process" not department. Contractors may provide support processes. In the short term all processes are candidates for improvement, but periodic redesign may be called for. There are different methodologies for each.

DEFINE CUSTOMER REQUIREMENTS is next. Who are customers of each process and what do they require? The Voice of the Customer must be heard through a variety of sources. Requirements may be for an output from the process or for a service as part of the process, typically both. The Kano model, categorising into basics, performance-related, or delighters, is useful. A SIPOC chart (suppliers, inputs, process, outputs, customers) is useful.

Then MEASURE PERFORMANCE. Go to gemba. Collect the facts, not opinions. An early step is to measure the measurement system, called Gage R&R. Define the customer critical measures, not the organisation critical measures. Give preference to continuous measures rather than discrete (yes/no) measures. How late, not if late. Measure the variability. Use statistical tests. The measure to be used for each process should be carefully defined in terms of what to measure, where, when and frequency of collection. Calculate the defect opportunities, and hence calculate the defects per million opportunities – Six Sigma aims at 3.4 DPMO and reduced variation. Note variation is a big killer: far better to be consistently one day late with delivery than sometimes one week early, sometimes one week late but OK on average. For many, a four sigma level may be adequate.

Now you can begin the DMAIC cycle: Define, Measure, Analyse, Improve, Control. There are standard steps, questions and procedures for each step depending on whether improvement or redesign is called for. An addition is Transfer, where what is achieved in one area is transferred to others. There may be an intranet for this.

A range of well-established quality and statistical methods provides SUPPORT for Six Sigma. Normally there will be a Quality Council or similar steering group. One feature is strong bottom line linkage to translate improvements into money and another, a trained hierarchy of experts, from Green Belt to Master Black Belt, undertakes projects.

Note the linkage diagram for six sigma – many areas in this book are relevant.

Many Six Sigma projects can gain huge benefit by starting with Lean on standards, mapping, 5S, layout, changeover, then doing the six sigma project, and then following up with more lean – again standard work, but also pokayoke, visibility, and heijunka.

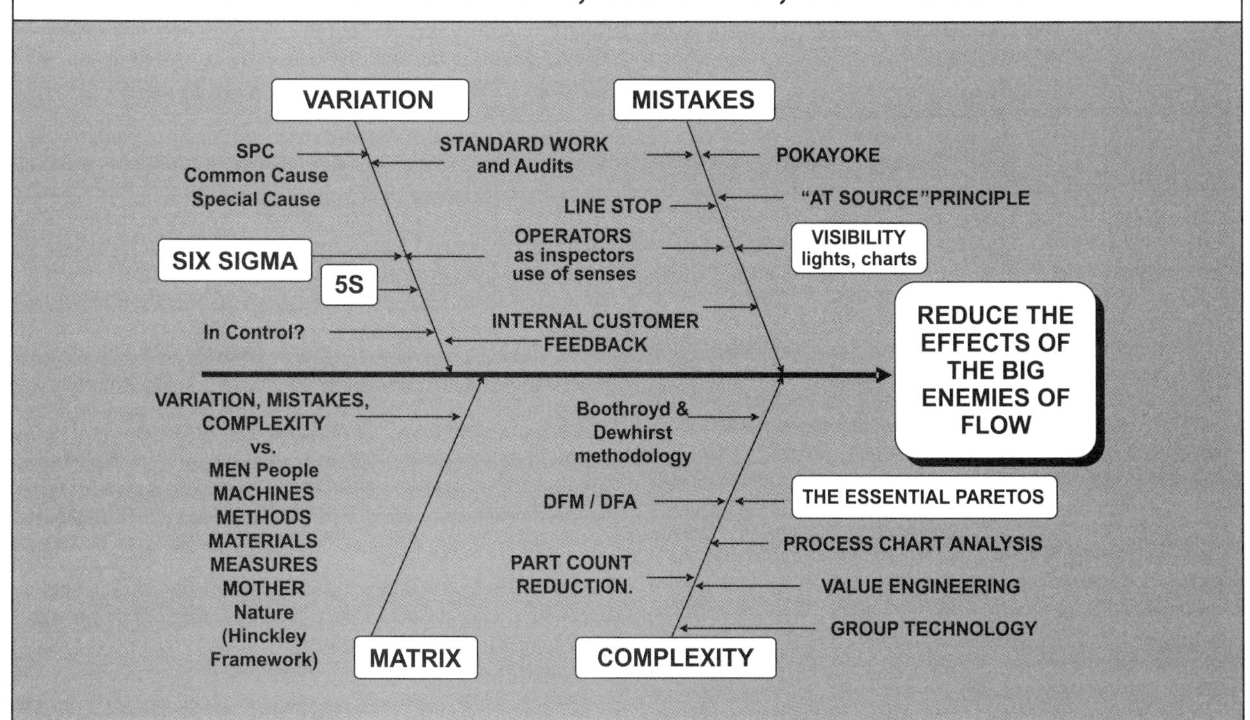
REDUCE VARIATION, MISTAKES, COMPLEXITY
VARIATION
MISTAKES
SPC
Common Cause
Special Cause
STANDARD WORK
and Audits
POKAYOKE
"AT SOURCE"PRINCIPLE
LINE STOP
SIX SIGMA
5S
OPERATORS
as inspectors
use of senses
VISIBILITY
lights, charts
In Control?
INTERNAL CUSTOMER
FEEDBACK
REDUCE THE
EFFECTS OF
THE BIG
ENEMIES OF
FLOW
VARIATION, MISTAKES,
COMPLEXITY
vs.
MEN People
MACHINES
METHODS
MATERIALS
MEASURES
MOTHER
Nature
(Hinckley
Framework)
Boothroyd &
Dewhirst
methodology
DFM / DFA
THE ESSENTIAL PARETOS
PROCESS CHART ANALYSIS
PART COUNT
REDUCTION.
VALUE ENGINEERING
GROUP TECHNOLOGY
MATRIX
COMPLEXITY

REDUCE VARIATION, MISTAKES and COMPLEXITY

C. Martin Hinckley suggested the powerful and comprehensive matrix of reducing variation, mistakes and complexity from all the M's – men/people, machines, methods, materials, measures, and perhaps mother nature. If all 3 x 6 = 18 cells can be addressed, you will have achieved a comprehensive improvement in quality and in flow. Hinckley suggests starting with products, progressing to processes, and lastly to tools. Each should go through steps of simplification, mistake proofing, and variation reduction.

Variation

Reducing variation has been highlighted by six sigma. There is no question that variation is the enemy of Lean. 5S and standard work play an important part. Understanding comes from collecting data on variation (say via SPC charts) and then distinguishing common cause from special cause.

Mistakes

Reducing variation is insufficient; mistakes can still arise however much variation is reduced. Pokayoke (mistake proof) devices are the prime means of reducing mistakes. Shingo gave three methods: contact (such as a protrusion that prevents incorrect orientation), motion step (which ensures that all steps have been completed, like order picking), and fixed value (like parts in an 'egg crate'). For each there are two types, control that stops work from proceeding, and warning that gives an alarm.

Operators, designers, engineers need to be given time and resources to develop mistake proofing devices.

Complexity

Reducing the part count, easing assembly complexity, using DFM/ DFA (Boothroyd and Dewhurst methods), and value engineering all contribute. Do take the opportunity periodically to examine the variety of parts, fasteners, spares, consumables. And options. And ask customers about their needs: do they really want that colour or would they prefer a slightly different but standardised colour at a reduced price. Do they really need that functionality. And, Japanese style, what would be the cost and advantage of giving everyone a 'full house' of options.

Further reading

C Martin Hiinckley, *Make No Mistake!*, Productivity, 2002

MAINTAIN THE PROCESSES for Flow

AWARENESS

OEE
measured
(beware!)

SIX BIG LOSSES
breakdown, c/over,
minor stops, reduced
speed, defectives,
c/over scrap

BATH TUB
CURVE STAGES
burn-in (reduce risk)
stable (extend life)
wear-out (planned maint)

PEOPLE

MAINTENANCE
PROS
procedures,
improvement,
training, more
complex tasks

AUTONOMOUS MAINTENANCE
operator ownership
use of senses, basic tasks
7 steps of autonomous maintenance

RED TAG Board

5S
practised

MACHINES,
TOOLS,
EQUIPMENT
HIGH OEE at
LOW
COST

BOARDS
Kamishibai, One
Point Lessons

MAINTENANCE
SHIFTS
bottleneck
priority,
regularity

CONDITION
MONITORING
failure type
awareness

DO NOT REWARD MAINTENANCE
REWARD NO MAINTENANCE

FAST RESPONSE
MTTR
lights, sound,
tool location,
response
time control

SUPPORT

VISIBLE
STANDARDS
on machines
on shop floor
auto counts

MIS
inventory, history,
maintenance cycles
timely replacement

DATA

MAINTAIN THE PROCESSES for Flow

For Lean, machines, tools and equipment have to be available without fail when needed. Of course, cost is also important but if everyone participates, these two aims are not trade-offs. Total productive maintenance (TPM) emphasises that the concept goes beyond prevention to include improvement in productivity. Total productive maintenance has much in common with total quality. Both encourage participation by both experts and operators, both emphasise ownership, both take a process view, both rely on good housekeeping.

TPM can be seen alongside the classic bath tub failure curve. At the burn-in stage, risk is reduced. In the stable stage, life is extended and the failure rate reduced. At the burn-out stage, planned maintenance is used.

Awareness: the starting point

Start with a 'spot the rot' exercise where the smallest 'out of place' or 'anything wrong' is noted, usually dozens in a small area.

OEE or overall equipment effectiveness is defined as availability % x performance rate % x yield rate %. This is a comprehensive view. Many companies display OEE graphs near critical machines: an overall graph and three supporting graphs, one for each factor. Below may be shown fishbone diagrams of contributing causes. Some management insist on OEE data before authorising capital expenditure; it may be better to improve rather than buy.

Six Big Losses are the elements of OEE: awareness helps to prioritise.

Red Tags provide visible awareness of maintenance requirements. Tags, sometimes with dates, are hung on a board and returned to the machine when the required maintenance is complete providing immediate visual impact of a backlog.

People: TPM is ultimately a people programme

Autonomous Maintenance means operator responsibility for own machines and operators carrying out as much routine maintenance work as possible. However, autonomous does not mean voluntary. People come with built-in noise detection, vision, and vibration detection equipment. So use these precious capabilities and get operators to report anything unusual. 5S (see separate figure) is an excellent way to involve people in TPM. Note: the term "autonomous maintenance" is used by Japan Institute of Plant Maintenance and includes 7 steps: cleanup, stop sources of defects, formulate standards, overall checkup, inside checkup, orderliness and tidiness, and ongoing improvement – roughly similar to 5S.

One-point lessons are TPM learning points for operators, where just one point is covered on a chart or sheet of paper. Focused learning. They are applicable not only in maintenance.

Maintenance professionals should do the more skilled tasks. As

they do this, OEE performance increases and a positive feedback loop is established. Freeing time should allow more operator training, and so on. The maintenance professionals in consultation with operators should work out standard procedures.

Support

Maintenance Shifts are a possibility in non-24/7 operations but routine maintenance is essential everywhere. Bottlenecks should enjoy priority. A regular cycle of preventive maintenance should be sustained and recorded where appropriate (below).

A refurbishment plan, aiming to go beyond just routine preventive maintenance, where machines enjoy a new lease of life, is developed in accordance with usage.

'Cleaning is Checking' should become the norm. Whilst cleaning, also check. As with your car, you don't check oil, tyres and water every time you drive – but you do so when you clean your car at the weekend.

Condition Monitoring monitors characteristics such as vibration and oil content to predict maintenance requirements. Failure type awareness is important for preventive maintenance; some machines have a "bathtub" failure mode, others L shaped, others flat, others reverse L. Knowing the failure mode determines whether PM is a good idea and when to do it.

Fast Response and Mean Time to Repair are possibly more important than mean time to failure because variation is reduced. Hence monitor and record MTTR. Use red tags. Use light and sound to draw attention. Toyota plays operator-selected tunes. Tool location should reflect frequency of use.

Data

Visible Standards for maintenance should be kept by machines, using photographs and sketches. Even better, show normal settings on the machine itself. Use automatic part counters to change tools and replace parts with a known frequency.

Information Systems play an important role to record breakdown and problem data for subsequent improvement target actions or optimal replacement decisions.

'Best of the Best' Analysis

Best of the best analysis is useful to overcome sceptics and show the possibilities. If you have several similar machines record the three elements of OEE separately for each machine over a number of days or weeks. Then find the best achievement on any machine on each of availability, performance, and quality. Multiply these 'bests' together to give a best of the best figure for your machines demonstrated on your site. If you have do not have like machines, record the best performance on each of the three elements each day and find the best ever achievement on each element. Multiply to get best of the best – that sets a demonstrated benchmark.

TPM Project Categories

Distinguish between projects aiming for Safety, for Appearance, and for OEE. Get operators to suggest projects under each heading.

A Note on OEE

OEE is a measure of great potency, but requires considerable caution.

An example: A shift takes 9 hours. Working time is 8 hours after planned maintenance and meeting time of one hour. Breakdowns take 20 minutes. Changeovers take 40 minutes. The standard machine cycle time is one minute. At the end of the day 350 parts have been made of 50 are scrapped.

Availability = (8x60 – 20 – 40)/ 8x60 = 88%
Performance: actual work time = 7 hours = 420 minutes, during which 420 should have been produced, so 350/420 = 83%
Quality: 300/350 = 86%
OEE = 88% x 83% x 86% = 63%

A boast like 'we have improved OEE by 20% should be treated with caution: (a) is it overproducing? (b) is it a bottleneck? (c) is it because bigger batches are being made? (d) is it producing the products that customers require? (e) by how much has regular maintenance time or cost increased?

There is no such thing as a 'world class' OEE level – it depends on the industry. Garbage vehicles cannot be compared with long runs in a clean room. OEE should be tracked on a graph – ideally with control limits to distinguish special causes from common causes. The trend is more important than the number.

The more your aggregate OEE, the further you get from real root causes – so calculating OEE for groups of machines is often a waste of time.

Note also that assigning losses by time (as in OEE) is not the same as losses by cost. So, scrap time maybe low but cost may be high.

Finally a quote: "Put all machinery in the best possible condition, keep it that way and insist on absolute cleanliness everywhere in order that a man may learn to respect his tools, his surroundings, and himself." Henry Ford, *Today and Tomorrow.*

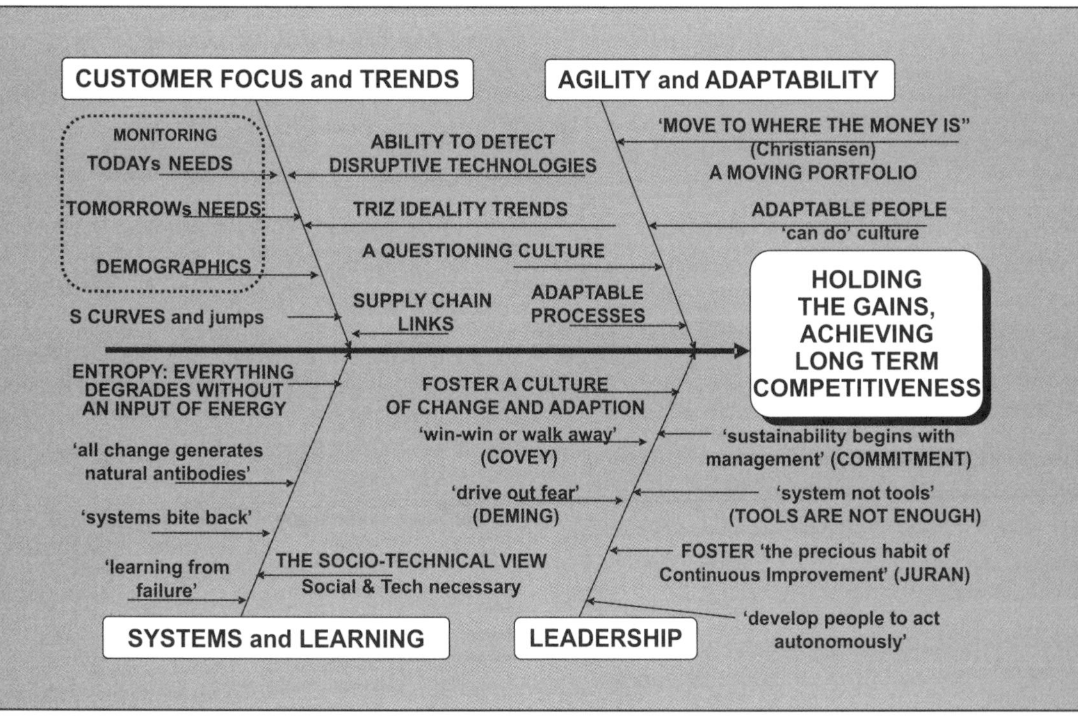
SUSTAINING Flow
CUSTOMER FOCUS and TRENDS
MONITORING
TODAYs NEEDS
TOMORROWs NEEDS
DEMOGRAPHICS
S CURVES and jumps
ABILITY TO DETECT DISRUPTIVE TECHNOLOGIES
TRIZ IDEALITY TRENDS
A QUESTIONING CULTURE
SUPPLY CHAIN LINKS
AGILITY and ADAPTABILITY
'MOVE TO WHERE THE MONEY IS" (Christiansen)
A MOVING PORTFOLIO
ADAPTABLE PEOPLE
'can do' culture
ADAPTABLE PROCESSES
HOLDING THE GAINS, ACHIEVING LONG TERM COMPETITIVENESS
ENTROPY: EVERYTHING DEGRADES WITHOUT AN INPUT OF ENERGY
'all change generates natural antibodies'
'systems bite back'
'learning from failure'
THE SOCIO-TECHNICAL VIEW
Social & Tech necessary
SYSTEMS and LEARNING
FOSTER A CULTURE OF CHANGE AND ADAPTION
'win-win or walk away' (COVEY)
'drive out fear' (DEMING)
'sustainability begins with management' (COMMITMENT)
'system not tools' (TOOLS ARE NOT ENOUGH)
FOSTER 'the precious habit of Continuous Improvement' (JURAN)
'develop people to act autonomously'
LEADERSHIP

SUSTAINING Flow

Sustainability has become the 'big issue' for experienced Lean organizations. There is no simple answer. Virtually all organizations, big or small, fail or cease sooner or later. Sustainability is an issue on all levels from workplace to organization, and beyond.

At all levels, the 5 words of Stephen Covey are fundamental to sustainability, 'win, win or walk away'. Both sides, customer & supplier, manager & operator, investor & organization, management & union, husband & wife, must win, somehow, or the organisation will not be sustained.

Customer Focus

Customers change. To sustain means to keep track of customer needs and to anticipate tomorrows needs. A clue is demographics: the next generations of customers have already been born. It is 'disruptive technologies' (Christensen) that are particularly troubling; these come from unexpected, frequently rejected, sources, grow quietly and suddenly emerge like Amazon or PCs. The TRIZ 'ideality' trends towards 'free, perfect, and now (an example is Google) seem relentless. Is there a way to leapfrog like cell phones in Africa? S-curves are universal – slow takeoff, growth, maturity, decline – only the time period varies. Then a new S curve arises, often with lower performance but higher potential. It takes courage to take a step back. Was this the early history of Lean?

Agility and Adaptability

It is not easy to 'move to where the money is' (Christensen) because of legacy systems and products. Different players along the total value stream make the money at different stages, the distributor, the manufacturer, the supplier, the designer. So, can the people and processes be made adaptable enough to respond? Writing scenarios is one possibility.

Systems and Learning

Remember the law of entropy: everything runs down unless energy is put in. And from biology, 'all change generates natural antibodies'. So unexpected opposition should be expected! Systems are socio-technical, and equal weight must be given to hard (tools, methods, procedures) and soft (people and customers). 'It is the soft stuff that is the hard stuff'.

Feedback seems crucial: the expectancy theory of motivation teaches that people learn how their actions affect outcomes and how outcomes affect rewards. So people must be grown with supportive feedback.

Leadership

Leaders have the vital role of fostering a culture of accepting change, and of fostering the 'precious habit of improvement' (Juran). Set aside time to 'sharpen the axe' every day. See the transformation fishbone.

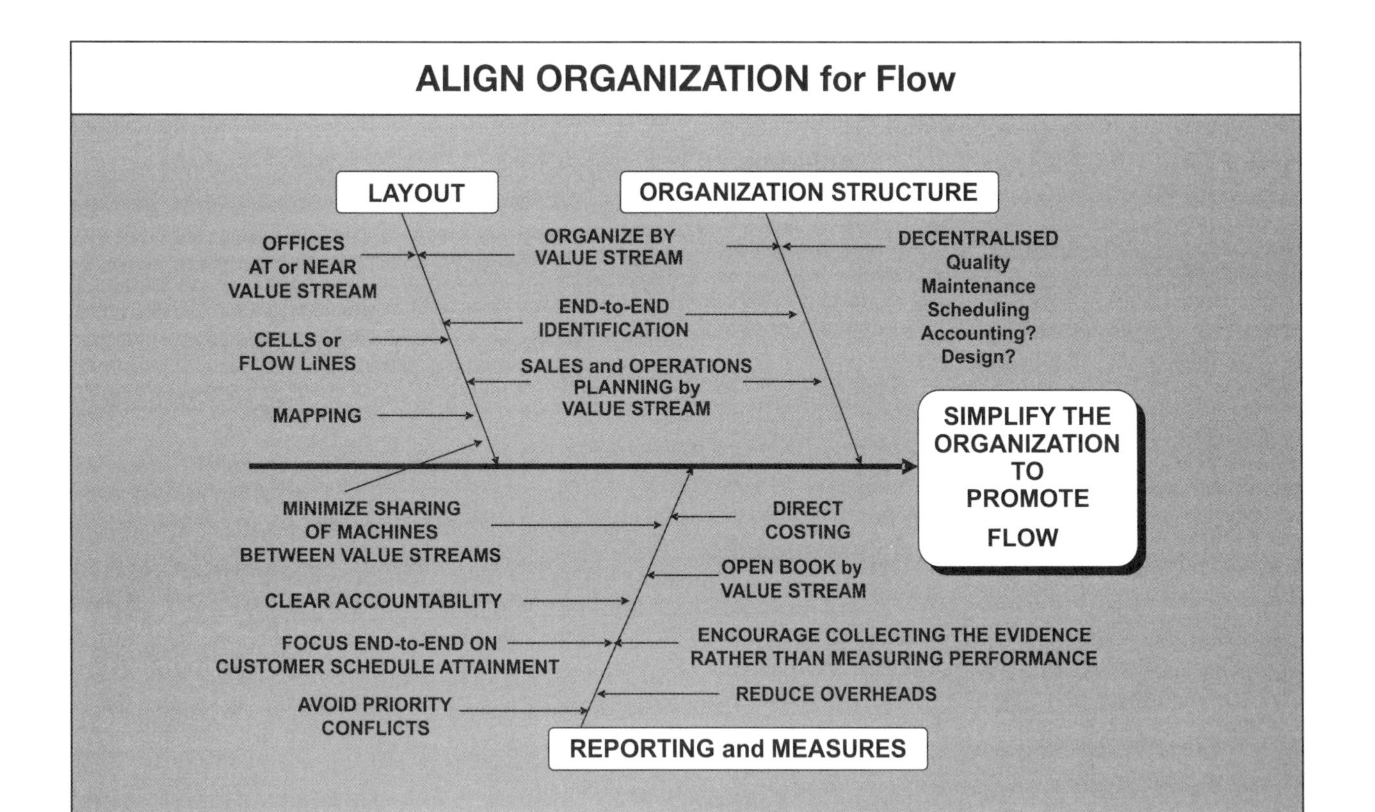
ALIGN ORGANIZATION for Flow
LAYOUT
ORGANIZATION STRUCTURE
OFFICES AT or NEAR VALUE STREAM
ORGANIZE BY VALUE STREAM
DECENTRALISED
Quality
Maintenance
Scheduling
Accounting?
Design?
END-to-END IDENTIFICATION
CELLS or FLOW LiNES
SALES and OPERATIONS PLANNING by VALUE STREAM
MAPPING
SIMPLIFY THE ORGANIZATION TO PROMOTE FLOW
MINIMIZE SHARING OF MACHINES BETWEEN VALUE STREAMS
DIRECT COSTING
OPEN BOOK by VALUE STREAM
CLEAR ACCOUNTABILITY
FOCUS END-to-END ON CUSTOMER SCHEDULE ATTAINMENT
ENCOURAGE COLLECTING THE EVIDENCE RATHER THAN MEASURING PERFORMANCE
REDUCE OVERHEADS
AVOID PRIORITY CONFLICTS
REPORTING and MEASURES

ALIGN THE ORGANIZATION for Flow

Very few if any organizations, Lean or otherwise, can survive without consistent alignment of the organization with goals and policies. But for flow, this is particularly important.

Layout

Layout is the obvious, visible manifestation of alignment. Organise by value streams. Have as few overhead functions as possible unassigned to value streams. Have offices near or at the Gemba or value stream. Perhaps even have a specific uniform for each area. Dedicate cells and flow lines to particular value streams. Each should have its own sales and operations planning (S&OP) function. Sharing machines between value steams complicates reporting, measures and clarity. It may take time to phase this out, but make it an aim.

Organization Structure

The structure must complement the layout. Try to align all 'overhead' functions with particular value streams, maintenance, quality, accounting, engineering, design, sales, even HR and the lean promotion office. Minimise shared resources of all types, human and machine. Perhaps a matrix structure is necessary but have the prime alignment with the value stream rather than the functional department.

Give the value stream organization decentralised responsibility for end-to-end flow. If end-to-end cannot be achieved, go as far as possible.

Peter Wickens, ex Nissan UK HR, talks about the ascendant organization that has both high commitment to people AND strong control over process and systems. Both aspects are important for a Lean aligned organization, but both take time and commitment to build.

The John Oakland TQM model can be adjusted for the Lean organization. At the centre is the end-to-end process chain, aligned for flow. Supporting this are systems, teams, and tools. These are, in turn, embedded in concerns for culture, communication and (longer term) commitment.

Reporting and Measures

Policy deployment is the prime tool for aligning measures. Reporting needs to be direct, as does costing, perhaps even using open book methods to all in a value stream.

The measures must be consistent with what the value stream is trying to achieve. This is focus. Measures must support flow, not batch and queue. Don't reward local performance that leads to sub-optimisation. Examples are warehouse inventory turns, call centre performance, sales. Instead, focus on customer satisfaction.

Lean and IMPROVEMENT

MAPPING
"LEARNING to SEE" Maps
Current State
Future State
VALUE ADD analysis
Analysis against TAKT time
OTHER MAPS
Demand Amplification
Time Cost Profile
Process Activity
Lead time
Quality Filter
Spaghetti

MATERIALS
LINE STOP
INVENTORY WITHDRAWAL win, win

MUDA Spectacles

THE FIVE WHYS

CONTINUOUSLY REDUCE WASTES

THE SEVEN WASTES

KAIZEN
'There is no best, there is only better' (Ohno)
MANAGEMENT preventing waste
SUPERVISORS facilitating waste removal
OPERATORS keeping waste out

METHODS
RESPONSE ANALYSIS
AUDIT AGAINST STANDARDS
PDCA ESTABLISHED
6 HONEST MEN
PROCESS WASTE CHECKLISTS
GEMBA
ONE POINT LESSONS
KAIZEN BLITZ Events
SIX SIGMA
KOBAYASHI 20 keys

Lean and IMPROVEMENT

At the heart of Lean improvement lie four basics:

- first, make everyone continuously aware of the 7 wastes, based on those suggested by Taiichi Ohno. These are shown on a separate figure. Dan Jones encourages people to "wear their Muda spectacles".
- second, encourage everyone to have a questioning attitude and to use the five whys.
- third is Kaizen, which is a belief in on-going improvements, made project by project by teams and consolidated, rather than a few big improvements made by "experts". Kaizen is complementary to break through improvements such as Kaizen Blitz.
- fourth, is continuous improvement through one improvement leading to another leading to another. Ohno is reputed to have said "there is no best, there is only better!".

MAPPING

Mapping is the way to direct improvements rather than leaping in in a haphazard fashion. "Learning to See" or brown paper mapping is a high-level mapping tool to identify problems and opportunities from supplier to customer. How the current state is to be transformed into the future state is directed by a series of questions relating to takt time, bottlenecks, location of buffers and supermarkets, and the possibilities of flow and pull. Normally, both short-term and long-term opportunities are identified. Value add analysis determines the proportions of time and activities that are value adding, non value adding, and temporary but necessary non value adding.

Other maps: *Demand amplification maps* track actual performance of orders and batches at each stage of manufacturing against time. The amplification of orders and the consistency of the schedule can be tracked. *Time cost profiles* track the cost build up of value adding and non-value adding activity against time. Plateaus indicate areas of inactivity, and the divergence of the two lines indicates the build up of waste. *Process activity maps* are the traditional industrial engineering tools of detailed activity analysis, classifying each activity into operation, delay, inspect, etc and are used to home in on areas of special concern. *The lead time map* identifies how lead-time is broken down. It will frequently be the case that most time is used off the factory floor. *The spaghetti diagram* traces the physical movement of parts.

MATERIALS

Deliberate inventory withdrawal encourages improvement by seeking to expose the next most limiting factor. The concept is that inventory covers up unseen problems. Remove some inventory and experiment! Identify the problem thus exposed and work on it. Inventory can be reduced by removing a kanban card or by cutting a kanban quantity. Supervisors or teams should suggest where cuts could be attempted. This is a "win win" strategy; either inventory is reduced or waste is identified. This is one way to continue with lean implementation: begin "loose" and gradually tighten. However, a safer approach for lean beginners is to identify

IMPROVEMENT CATEGORIES

	INCREMENTAL 'Point Kaizen'	BREAKTHROUGH 'Flow Kaizen'	EXECUTION
	Suggestion Schemes Self Directed Teams Quality Circles Open Book Mgmt, 5S, Waste awareness	Industrial Engineering O.R. (Some) Six Sigma	PASSIVE / ENABLED
	Line stop, Andon, Heijunka, Visual Mgmt, Inventory withdrawal, 'Chalk circle',Red Tags Six Sigma projects Kaizen events	Value Stream Mapping Supply Chain Development	DRIVEN / ENFORCED
	DFM / DFA Group Technology Value Eng D.O.E.	3-D Simulation Location decisions Set based design Target Costing	PREPARATION

TRIZ

TRIZ

problems first (say by mapping), remove problems, and then reduce inventory.

METHODS

A basic approach is to "go to gemba" and collect the facts. Standards are the building block for continuous improvement. Standards should be audited and deviations identified. The idea is not to be a policeman but to build on best-known and safest way. Process waste checklists are prepared by the lean promotion office and issued to everyone including office workers. These lists contain questions such as "do you walk to pick up parts?" If yes, there is waste and you are challenged on how to reduce it. Another form of audit is the Kobayashi 20 key questionnaire that identifies the areas of strength and weakness and provokes improvement ideas.

Use Kipling's 6 Honest Serving Men: '... who taught me all I knew; their names are what and why and when, and where and how and who'.

Kaizen Blitz events are given a separate fishbone, but many kaizens can be done in a few minutes or hours. Imai's 'kaizen flag' shows everyone, managers and operators, devoting some time to kaizen every week. Management is concerned with designing value in and keeping waste out, supervisors with getting waste out, operators with keeping waste out.

Six Sigma (see separate section) is a major alternative focusing on the reduction of variation and improvement.

IMPROVEMENT CATEGORIES

There is 'point kaizen', concerned with local improvement. And there is 'flow kaizen' concerned with value stream improvement.

'Execution' is of two types: passive (left to the own initiative of operators, industrial engineers, and managers), and enforced or driven (such as the concepts given under the problem surfacing fishbone earlier). This gives four categories of improvement. All are necessary; all are found in the best Lean companies. This is getting the waste out, and keeping it out.

Then there is 'Preparation' at the design stage, both passive and enforced. This then gives a total of six categories. This is preventing waste from entering in the first place.

TRIZ ideas (or the theory of inventive problem solving) are useful throughout. TRIZ helps one to draw on the best, most relevant, innovations that have ever been made.

In each category there are good and not so good ways of doing things. The not so good involves an arrogant, self-seeking approach. The good uses participation, listening, patience, humility, recognition, and feedback.

THE SEVEN WASTES after Taiichi Ohno

T	**TRANSPORT**	all materials movement, double handling
I	**INVENTORY**	stores, buffers, batches and their control systems
M	**MOTION**	reaching, bending, exertion, excess walking excessive turns to loosen, unpack
W	**WAITING**	materials queuing, not moving people not productively employed expediting
O	**OVERPROCESSING**	too fast, too big, too variable one big machine instead of several smaller
O	**OVERPRODUCING**	too early, too much, just-in-case
D	**DEFECTS**	rework, rejects, unnecessary inspection; consequences of not doing it right the first time

SEVEN WASTES and SEVEN SERVICE WASTES

These are given on successive figures.

Ohno's original seven wastes can be remembered by the acronym TIM WOOD. To the seven can be added an eighth waste, the waste of human potential, ninth, the waste of making the wrong product perfectly, tenth, the waste of inappropriate systems (ERP and the like), and eleventh, the waste of natural resources, water, power, materials, etc.

Note, however, that Ohno did not start with the list of wastes and then go out and seek them. He started with the vision of what was needed and identified the wastes that were in the way. This is far better! A 'waste walk' may be just that, a waste of time.

With recognition that most manufactures are part of a product-service bundle, a list of seven service wastes is proposed. See next figure.

KAIZEN EVENTS and Flow

Kaizen events (or Blitz) have, for some become a routine way of progressing Lean. Many events are 5 days, but one, two or three day events are also common. We have learned that preparation and follow up are as least as important as the event itself.

Good events follow a pre-identified need flowing out of a bigger picture such as via a value stream map or hoshin exercise. For some, regularity is a key, doing one event say every two weeks. Events require facilitation by a lean promotion office (LPO) or kaizen office, following the plan, do, check, act cycle. Deming said 'do' was one quarter of the PDCA cycle; that is good advice for kaizen events also. Take time to plan, to learn, to standardise or hold the gains.

Preparation

Choice of the team is critical; it must contain the supervisor and first line manager. Senior managers must be briefed even if they are not due to take part in order to give blanket approval, to encourage, to empower. The aim must be specific and clear, like lead time or visibility, and not a general 'improvement'. A pre-diagnostic day or two is required to scope the event, do preliminary mapping, data collection, clarification, and barrier identification. Preparation also includes standby maintenance and support functions. The base measures are established.

The Event

A day by day, if not more detailed, plan is required. Sub teams record and do the analysis work. Everyone is involved. There is a 'just do it now' culture: do bold things, shift the furniture. Measure progress every day. Do a mini PDCA each day. Conclude with a presentation, a follow up list, and recognition. Document and photograph. Display on a standard form.

SEVEN SERVICE WASTES

DUPLICATION	Re-enter data, store in several locations
WAITING for SERVICE	for service, in queues, for delivery, for response, not arriving as promised
INCORRECT INVENTORY	out-of-stock, unable to get exactly what was required
UNNECESSARY MOVEMENT	queuing several times, no one-stop, poor ergonomics or layout in the service encounter
UNCLEAR COMMUNICATION	failure demand, seeking clarification, confusion over product or service use
OPPORTUNITY LOST	to retain or win customers, not listening, lack of empathy or responsiveness
ERRORS	in the service transaction, in the product-service bundle, lost or damaged goods

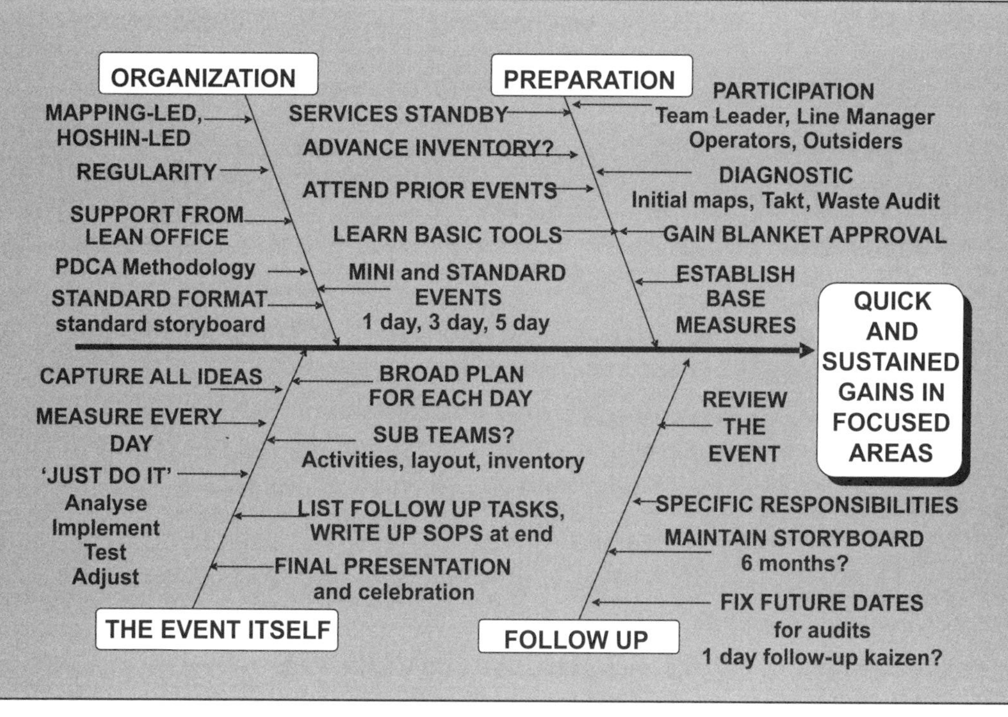
Flow and KAIZEN EVENTS
ORGANIZATION
MAPPING-LED, HOSHIN-LED
REGULARITY
SUPPORT FROM LEAN OFFICE
PDCA Methodology
STANDARD FORMAT standard storyboard
SERVICES STANDBY
ADVANCE INVENTORY?
ATTEND PRIOR EVENTS
LEARN BASIC TOOLS
MINI and STANDARD EVENTS 1 day, 3 day, 5 day
PREPARATION
PARTICIPATION Team Leader, Line Manager Operators, Outsiders
DIAGNOSTIC Initial maps, Takt, Waste Audit
GAIN BLANKET APPROVAL
ESTABLISH BASE MEASURES
QUICK AND SUSTAINED GAINS IN FOCUSED AREAS
CAPTURE ALL IDEAS
MEASURE EVERY DAY
'JUST DO IT' Analyse Implement Test Adjust
BROAD PLAN FOR EACH DAY
SUB TEAMS? Activities, layout, inventory
LIST FOLLOW UP TASKS, WRITE UP SOPS at end
FINAL PRESENTATION and celebration
THE EVENT ITSELF
REVIEW THE EVENT
SPECIFIC RESPONSIBILITIES
MAINTAIN STORYBOARD 6 months?
FIX FUTURE DATES for audits 1 day follow-up kaizen?
FOLLOW UP

STANDARD WORK for Flow

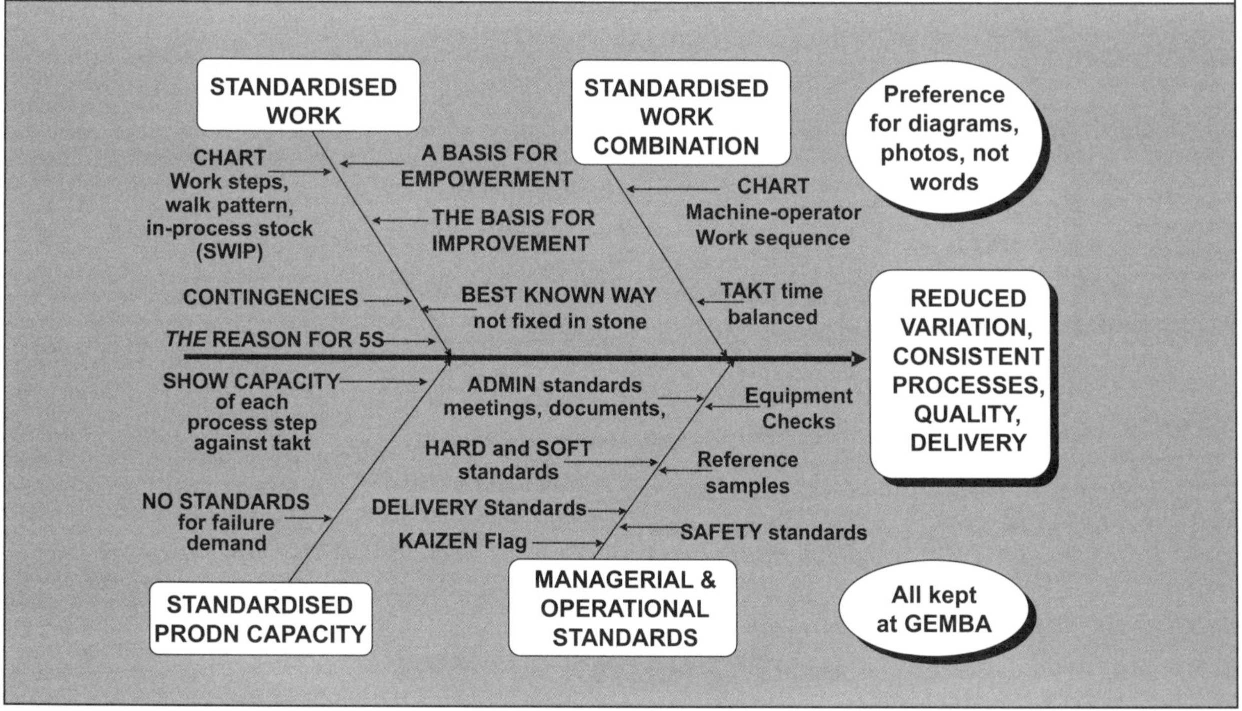

STANDARDISED WORK

CHART
Work steps,
walk pattern,
in-process stock
(SWIP)

A BASIS FOR
EMPOWERMENT

THE BASIS FOR
IMPROVEMENT

CONTINGENCIES

BEST KNOWN WAY
not fixed in stone

THE REASON FOR 5S

STANDARDISED WORK COMBINATION

CHART
Machine-operator
Work sequence

TAKT time
balanced

Preference for diagrams, photos, not words

REDUCED VARIATION, CONSISTENT PROCESSES, QUALITY, DELIVERY

SHOW CAPACITY
of each
process step
against takt

ADMIN standards
meetings, documents,

HARD and SOFT
standards

NO STANDARDS
for failure
demand

DELIVERY Standards

KAIZEN Flag

Equipment
Checks

Reference
samples

SAFETY standards

STANDARDISED PRODN CAPACITY

MANAGERIAL & OPERATIONAL STANDARDS

All kept at GEMBA

STANDARD WORK for Flow

Standards are the building blocks for Lean, for Six Sigma, and for the Supply Chain. Continuous improvement needs to "hold the gains" (Juran) before moving forward, and standards prevent slipping backwards. We are not talking here about British Standards, MIL standards, ISO standards, Fire Standards and the like. Such standards tend to be fixed and given. We are talking here about operations standards – the current best, safest known way. Standards should be written by operators not work experts, but where necessary in consultation with supervisors and IE's; revised whenever necessary, followed between revisions, kept at the workplace (at "Gemba"), making best use of photos and sketches rather than words. There are generally four categories, the first three of which relate together to workplaces or cells.

Any time a standard is not being followed (for instance having more than the standard inventory) it is an indication that something unusual is happening. Action is called for.

STANDARDISED WORK charts set out the steps carried out by an operator in a process or in making a product. They include work steps, the layout walk pattern in the case of cells, and the standard in-process stock. Standard work should allow time for inspection, but generally no allowance for rest and delay, which should be taken at specific intervals not continually occurring at unspecified times. A standard work sheet should also contain the standard work in process (SWIP).

Standard work is not restrictive. Indeed, it is the opposite – like a soldier's 'rules of engagement' it gives the parameters of freedom to act.

Standard work is THE reason for 5S

STANDARDISED PRODUCTION CAPACITY turns standard times into the standard daily capacity. This is measured against takt time (the customer's rate of demand).

STANDARDISED WORK COMBINATION Chart is found in cells where operators tend several machines. The chart shows the time to load, unload and walk between machines. Machine cycles are also shown. An operator must be able to complete his work cycle within the takt time. This is the lean form of "man machine chart".

MANAGERIAL AND OPERATIONAL STANDARDS are found at Gemba throughout the rest of the organisation. There may be standards for meetings, for agendas, for delivery, for safety, for most things. This is safety, good management, order, and not bureaucracy. Both hard and soft standards are frequently necessary in admin and service – hard standards relate to materials and procedures, soft relate to customers and behaviours. Everyone has standards – especially managers!

VISUAL MANAGEMENT for FLOW

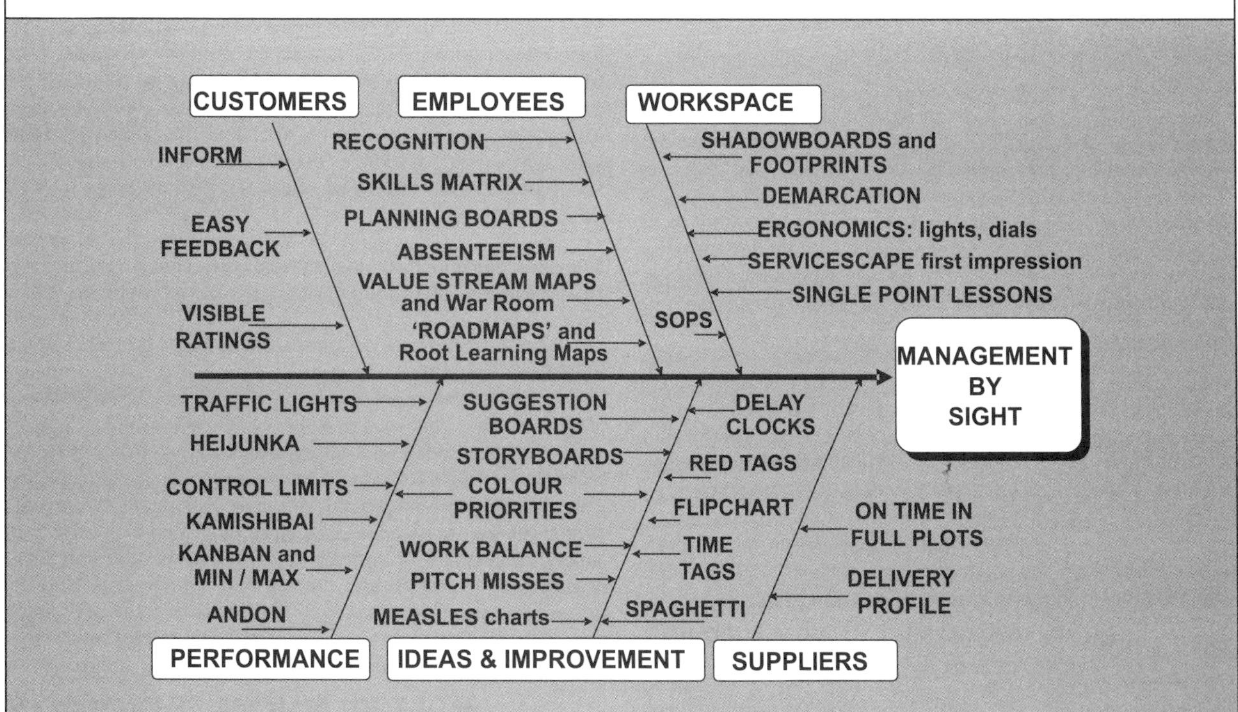

VISUAL MANAGEMENT for Flow

Visibility and simplicity are major characteristics of Lean. If you are guided by the maxim of managing by sight you will not go far wrong. Visibility means a change in management style from managing by remote control to managing by walking about. Visibility also implies simplicity – a workplace where anything out of order is immediately seen. For the Supply Chain, visibility means transparency of information upstream and downstream. Sharing demand, quality, customer, and design information upstream and downstream.

Customers

Understanding customers is the first lean principle. To do so means that feedback should be as easy as possible – for customers and employees. How? By visible customer ratings, by easy to complete feedback, by visual displays at shipping and receiving, by displays that communicate customer feedback –positive and negative – throughout the value stream.

Employees

A value stream 'war room' or 'green area' is a focus point for visual management. Maps and graphs on cost, quality and delivery are on display. Visual recognition of good performance, through idea and contribution boards, helps with motivation and momentum. Encourage employees to add their own items to the board. A skills matrix encourages development and assists with scheduling. Planning boards come in many forms – a voluntary what-everyone-is-doing in a design office, progress towards the future state, and a policy deployment matrix links local operations with wider priorities. Some record absenteeism visually. "Roadmaps' or 'root learning maps' are growing in popularity. These show where the company has come from, where it is going, and events and milestones along the route.

Performance

Traffic light displays of cost, quality and delivery give quick feedback. Schedules and counters such as Heijunka boards or production by the hour, guide and track performance for all to see. Graphs should have control limits to distinguish common from special causes. Kamishibai boards visually schedule routine maintenance across the week, requiring cards to be turned around when actions are done. Min/Max lines indicate inventory. Andon lights (and sirens) indicate problems. 5S boards (on display in the entrance?) indicate current scores, whether improving or declining, and photos of team and manager. Kanban cards are visual, and priorities can be indicated by colour. Graphing changeover times gives good incentive to retain consistency.

Workspace

Responsibilities for 5S should be clearly shown on maps or on the floor. Shadowboards and footprints indicate correct positions . Lights indicate out of control situations. Dials should be readable at a glance. Check points can be painted on the floor. Single point

lessons, on display at the gemba, show correct methods and remain until embedded. In service or customer facing operations, customer first impressions are important – hence attention to the 'servicescape' – a 5S from the customer's viewpoint.

Ideas and Improvement

Suggestion boards encourage improvement. Storyboards with standard format document success in kaizen events. Work balance boards are on display at cells, helping with work allocation. Pitch misses, used with heijunka, indicate how far behind the schedule is and who to call. Delay clocks do similarly for assembly lines. Such stoppages may be linked to a computer system that builds up a Pareto of accumulated problems.

Locating offices so that their occupants can be accessible and be seen is good policy. A trick is to locate design offices so that designers must cross the shop floor to get there. Common refreshment areas serve similar purposes. Red tags, with date and time, are placed on machines needing attention. Spaghetti diagrams are a powerful visual way to improve layout. And flipcharts are a visual way to accumulate problem events at gemba, building into a pareto. At Toyota tunes are played when machines breakdown; each machine has its own tune. SPC charts and other variation performance should be kept at the process. Likewise all forms of defect displays. Two-dimensional checklists, for instance showing operators on one-axis and defect types on the other give multi-dimensional information. Alternative axes may be time, product, process. A flipchart should be kept at every cell. Measles charts can be kept for products, for accident near misses, for suggestions, for stoppages and other possibilities. All build up into automatic Pareto charts. Fishbone diagrams can be used to summarise, as in this book.

Suppliers

Record delivery performance by on-time-in-full graphs, but also note reasons by adding post-its. At the receiving dock build a profile of 'put-away into inventory' times in order to reschedule to smooth the flow of work.

Other Areas

Hoshin Goals (the few critical goals to be achieved) should be clearly and prominently displayed. And how the company is performing against the targets should be on display.

Each team should maintain a set of statistics and graphs relating to their own performance. Better to let teams do this themselves than to have "professional" graphs plotted on a central computer. A skill matrix, showing progress from beginner to master in each skill category belongs in team areas. Names are shown on one axis and skills on the other axis. The contribution of team members to improvement is best shown at or near the workplace.

Some companies (e.g. Ford) give access to the Ford intranet from the shopfloor. This opens up huge information possibilities.

5S

5S is the basic housekeeping discipline for lean, quality and safety. It applies in office and on shop floor equally. Everyone has the experience of working better and feeling better in a tidy room. But it's also a mindset thing – changing attitudes from "I work in a dirty factory" to "I work in a manufacturing laboratory".

Sort

The first step is to establish the need for 5S – safety, consistency, quality, productivity. Take time on this, it is the key to later sustainability. Then classify literally everything by frequency. A good idea to do this with the team and to touch everything systematically. If used every day, is the quantity correct? If used weekly can it be brought out weekly? If used monthly should it rather be located in the store? If never, or in doubt, then red tag or throw out. A Red Tag is a label with the date; if no one accesses it within a specified period it should be thrown out.

Simplify

A place for everything - using shadowboards, inventory footprints, tools and dies on trolleys or at the right height, and colour matching to link associated tools, and everything in its place. If it is not there and not in use, that indicates a problem. Personal toolboxes are discouraged because you want the tools for the job at the job in standardised locations for operator flexibility. Arrange shadowboards and footprints. Consider lighting. Get after the sources of contamination. The standard is the "Dental Surgery". Why? Because everyone can relate to that standard of excellence. "One level" means trying to keep dies, tools and parts at the same level as the workplace to minimise bending. These first two steps need to be repeated periodically.

Sweep

This includes physical tidy up, on an ongoing basis, and "visual sweeping" whereby operators are always on the lookout for anything out of place, and try to correct it immediately. Some companies adopt a 5 minute routine whereby operators work out a 5 minute cleanup routine for each day of the week such that by week end everything has been covered the required number of times.

"Cleaning is Checking" means that these are integrated. You don't just clean up, you check for any abnormality and its root causes. Not just cleaning up the oil but asking why it is there in the first place.

Standardise

Establishing standards and SOPS should be the real reason, the 'bottom line' for 5S. Safety standards are also vital. Now SOPS can be written by operators for operators with guidance from supervisors and engineers.

Sustain

Sustain is the difficult one. Everyone needs to participate in 5S on an ongoing basis. Have audits. Have a floating trophy. Have

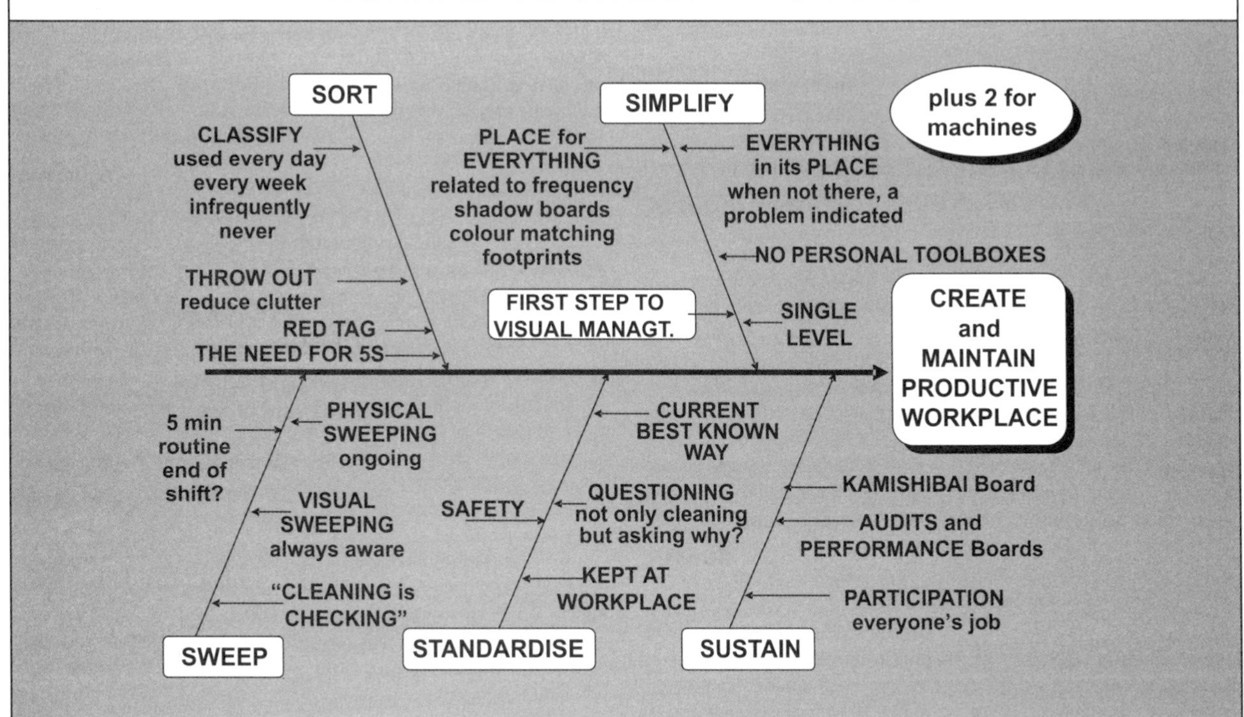
WORKPLACE ORGANIZATION & 5S
SORT
CLASSIFY
used every day
every week
infrequently
never
THROW OUT
reduce clutter
RED TAG
THE NEED FOR 5S
SIMPLIFY
PLACE for
EVERYTHING
related to frequency
shadow boards
colour matching
footprints
EVERYTHING
in its PLACE
when not there, a
problem indicated
NO PERSONAL TOOLBOXES
FIRST STEP TO
VISUAL MANAGT.
SINGLE
LEVEL
plus 2 for
machines
CREATE
and
MAINTAIN
PRODUCTIVE
WORKPLACE
SWEEP
5 min
routine
end of
shift?
PHYSICAL
SWEEPING
ongoing
VISUAL
SWEEPING
always aware
"CLEANING is
CHECKING"
STANDARDISE
CURRENT
BEST KNOWN
WAY
SAFETY
QUESTIONING
not only cleaning
but asking why?
KEPT AT
WORKPLACE
SUSTAIN
KAMISHIBAI Board
AUDITS and
PERFORMANCE Boards
PARTICIPATION
everyone's job

display boards of 5S performance for the whole company – offices and management areas included. Have teams visit and audit other areas. Show best practice. Emphasize safety. For maintenance, use a kamishibai board.

Note: Alternatives for 5S (but basically the same thing) are Simplify, Straighten, Scrub, Stabilise, Sustain or CANDO – Cleanup, Arrange, Neatness, Discipline, Ongoing improvement.

Wider 5S

How about doing 5S in offices? On computer files? On suppliers? In customer facing areas? On accounting transactions? On meetings?

Two Extra for Machines

The 7 steps of Autonomous Maintenance are very similar to 5S except that there are two additions (1) implementing countermeasures to defects (pokayoke and others) and sources of contamination and (2) autonomous internal checking, not just external as in 5S. The first of these follows the sort or cleanup stage and the second is done after external simplification.

LAYOUT for Flow

LOCATION
LOCATION SPAGHETTI of major components
CONCEPT mixed? near customer? dedicated line?
SUPPORT
DIE USE FREQUENCY
LINESIDE DELIVERY
SUPERMARKETS
FIFO Lanes
ACCESS to machines, inventory
SMALL MACHINES
MACHINES ON WHEELS
FOOTPRINTING and 5S
HUMAN-MOVABLE CONTAINERS
GRAVITY FEEDS
FLOW FACILITATION WITH MINIMUM WASTE
MEETING AREAS
FLOW LENGTH MONITORING
YAMAZUMI Board
3P
SPAGHETTI Diagram
WASTE CHECKLISTS
DYNAMIC LAYOUT
IMPROVEMENT
ONE-PIECE FLOW
TAKT TIME Balance
U SHAPE
PULSE LINE
FLOW LINE
"CHUKA-CHUKA"
AUTONOMOUS control
CELL CONCEPT
ERGONOMIC IMPACT measured; standing?
AUTONOMOUS areas
QUALITY of LIFE noise, light
WORKSTATIONS

LAYOUT for Flow

Layout sets the scene for Lean. Poor layout is perhaps the greatest ongoing source of waste and the greatest opportunity. Layout is a key facilitator because it makes small batch or one-piece-flow possible. By contrast, with non-lean layout there is no option but to move parts around in surging batches. Layout is also key to improved quality. So the over-riding layout principle is to move machines and processes closer together, as soon as and whenever opportunities arise. Opportunities always arise when buffer stock is reduced, when new machines are acquired, with new products, when changeover is reduced, and so on. Traditional re-layout tended to take place only periodically; with lean, layout changes are made much more frequently.

Layout should be thought of as a hierarchical process from plant location to factory layout, to cell layout, to workstation design.

Location

Begin with a spaghetti diagram showing how major components get moved around before arriving at the plant and after they leave. Calculate the speed of this movement and ask searching questions on transport, location and batch sizes.

Plant concept reminds one to look at whether one should consider a mixed plant serving several customers, dedicated customer cells or lines on own site, a dedicated focused plant near a major customer, or moving onto a customer's site. The same considerations apply in reverse to your major suppliers.

Support

There is a whole raft of concepts to aid lean layout. Machines on wheels offers ultimate flexibility but may not be practical. Die use frequency reminds us to locate more frequently used dies closer to machines that use them. Do a Pareto. Lineside delivery by suppliers is the ideal, but a supermarket may be an interim solution. Cells and lines should be balanced against takt time, using actual times without allowances. Cells or lines should be balanced to equalise work, but not to 100% of takt. Breaks are taken more frequently, and work is at standard rate or zero. The shojinka concept alters the number of operators depending on takt time. This makes cross training necessary. Containers should be human-movable if possible, or parts moved by gravity feed. Machines require access, particularly around the back. Inventory footprints should be shown. The Small Machine concept is a major facilitator. (See separate section.)

Cell Concept

The fundamental advantage of cells is one-piece flow. The reason is reduction in lead-time. If flow is not one-piece you do not have a lean cell! Inventory standards and SOPS should exist in every cell. A lean ideal is frequently U shape with operators within arms length. The cell leader works in the first and last operation. There may be a series of U cells. Cycle times less than about 20 seconds are undesirable for RSI, boredom, checking and improvement reasons. More than about 10 people in a cell prevents full cross training flexibility and works against the team concept. A chuka chuka line is a dedicated series of often automated small machines

that complete a component when necessary. A pulse line or moving line is for large, long cycle processes. Here the product moves slowly down a line or, for example, moves forward once per week. Nevertheless, within the long cycle work is planned hour by hour in standard work elements. Becoming popular are cells where operators each complete a full product over a few hours but work in parallel with common stocking points. A virtual cell is used if machines are too large to locate into a physical cell. Here operators from several sequential processes work as a team rather than for their own process department. Here, simplicity of control and reduced leadtime frequently more than compensate for any capacity loss.

Cells should be autonomous with integrated quality, maintenance, and sometimes schedule responsibility. Cells are often paced by heijunka or schedule-by-the-hour.

Workstations

Workstations need to be designed with their ergonomic impact and the waste of motion in mind. Minimise both horizontal movement and vertical movement of parts and tools. Standing may be better than sitting for flexibility and posture. Autonomous layout means full responsibility in designated areas. Quality of life should be improved by considering noise, light, floors, and of course safety.

Improvement

Begins by knowing flowlengths and trying to minimise. Spaghetti diagrams are powerful aids at factory and workstation level. Waste checklists, prepared by the lean promotion office, help to keep muda in mind. Meeting areas, in which performance is displayed, are great for teamwork and improvement. A flip chart to note problems immediately should be an essential item in every cell.

3P or production preparation process is a methodology that requires the cell or layout team, including operators, to develop several alternatives for each process step and to evaluate each alternative. Also known as cardboard trial it develops a full-scale mock up of the cell to collect times and de-bug.

DEVELOP PEOPLE and TEAMS for Flow

An ongoing theme in Lean must be growing and developing people and teams. Lean is team process. It requires new attitudes and practices by managers and operators. Trust on both sides has to be built over time. The aim is to create thinking, participating, stakeholders not mere employees. Toyota takes maybe six months to grow a new manager into a job.

Policy

A basic concept is to "hire the whole person" – his or her skills, brain, all the senses, and all the potential. Aim to hire people who are willing to contribute in this full way. Most will need to be team players. Participation has to become the norm – progress displays, newsletters, and team briefings all help. Line and staff equality, on benefits, facilities, conditions of employment, and even parking, fosters teamwork and communication, creates job security, and "drives out fear". Participation cannot include people improving themselves out of a job. But no company can guarantee ultimate job security, so everyone must understand the difference between the risks of the market and the security of making improvements. Training for lifetime skills is the ultimate job security for today's insecure market place. A company may not be able to guarantee job security but can help operators to build their marketability to benefit both company and themselves. Annualised hours helps with non-stable demand by calling in work as needed but guaranteeing minimum and maximum monthly and annual number of hours. A win for both company and operator. Fewer job categories leads to greater flexibility and improved security. The right attitude is more important than the right skills, many of which can be added later.

The 'hot stove' analogy is the family gathered around a stove (the company) that gives warmth and support. Moms and Dads listen carefully to kids and have their wellbeing and advancement as genuine priorities. But there is discipline also – the stove burns anyone who touches, but also has no memory.

PDCA means that people must learn the plan, do, check, act cycle of experimental method. Take time to plan, but also look back and review in order to learn more. This takes years to master, not minutes!

Capacity through people is the belief that capacity can be increased not only by extra machines and space, but also through people having greater and more flexible skills. Developing people is often more cost effective than buying physical plant.

Rewards and Incentives

Rewards and incentives must not compromise quality or encourage overproduction or any other wastes, but should encourage improvement. Gainsharing, with benefits shared on the basis of improvements, seems to be compatible with lean. But the big one is recognition – always thanks, sometimes celebrations, and recognition boards.

DEVELOP PEOPLE and TEAMS for FLOW (1)

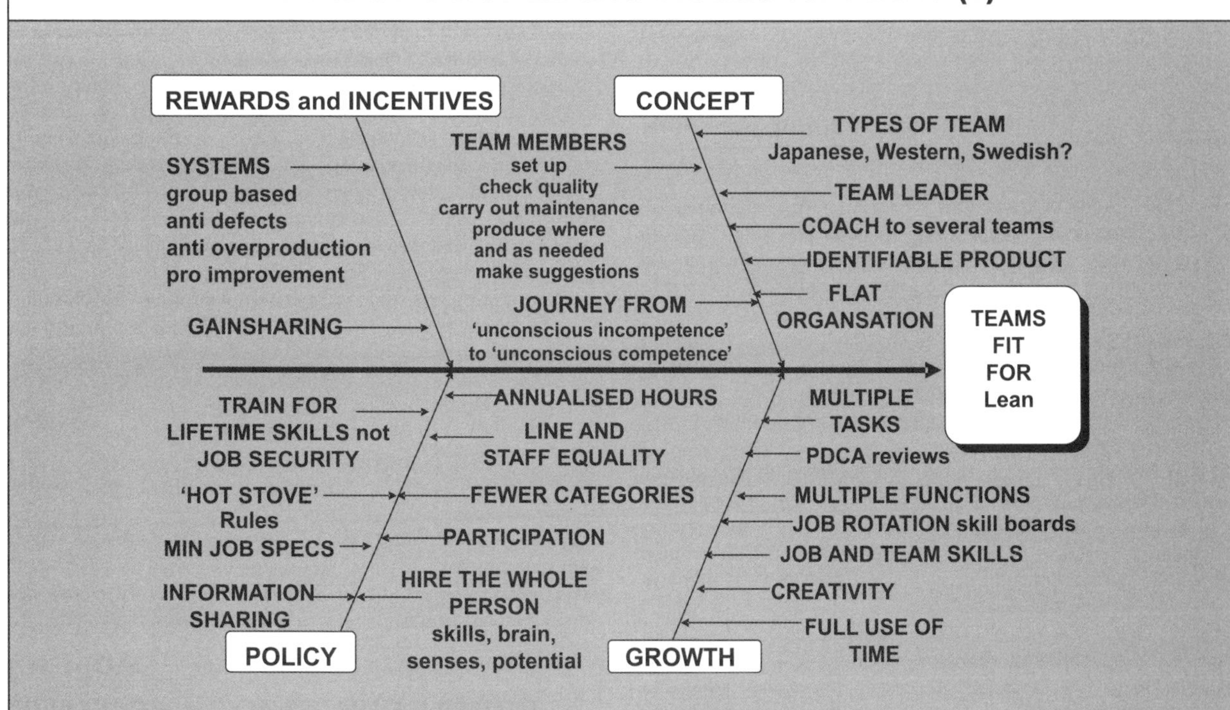

Incentive schemes need to reward the quantity of suggestions, not just the quality. The Pareto principle applies – a few good suggestions make a whole incentive scheme worthwhile, but to get to those few many need to be sifted through. This requires quick and positive response.

Concept

The team concept is one of the most important developments accompanying lean. It begins with operators that are multi-functional. This leads to quality of worklife – involvement, participation, security, and growth, even perhaps fun.

Edward Lawler's "Star" concept (People, Strategy, Structure, Processes, Rewards) is a useful checklist on areas that must be considered whilst setting up a team.

Teams evolve into self-direction, where team leaders are elected by and responsible to, the team not the company. At the same time former supervisors become coaches who decide with, rather than for, teams. Coaches are chosen by, and responsible to, management.

Note that there are three approaches to teams. The Japanese approach uses teams for improvement and the team may have responsibility for line balance, but the supervisor has authority for work allocation and team wellbeing. Here there may be quality circles – voluntary but permanent. Toyota also uses several other types of team, which are appointed for a specific purpose and disbanded at the end of the study. The Western approach goes further with self-direction. Here the team eventually assumes responsibility for many activities – with team leadership rotating depending upon the problem. The third approach is the "Swedish" model where teams build whole products or assemblies with very long cycle times. This approach has been abandoned by its originator, Volvo, but remains useful for some specialised tasks.

Growth

Skills should be displayed on a team matrix board using a U or other symbol that is filled in as team members progress from beginner to teacher. Training should include not only job skills, but also problem solving and teamworking skills.

Education and training should take place "just in time" linking theory with immediate practice. There is a cycle to identify the next skill, train for it, test, and consolidate before moving onto the next skill. Full use of time, means that in flexible plants there are always training or improvement activities running that can be slotted in when production targets have been reached.

Having developed the people and team (shown in the first figure), they are then involved in achieving high performance. Of course, this is an ongoing process.

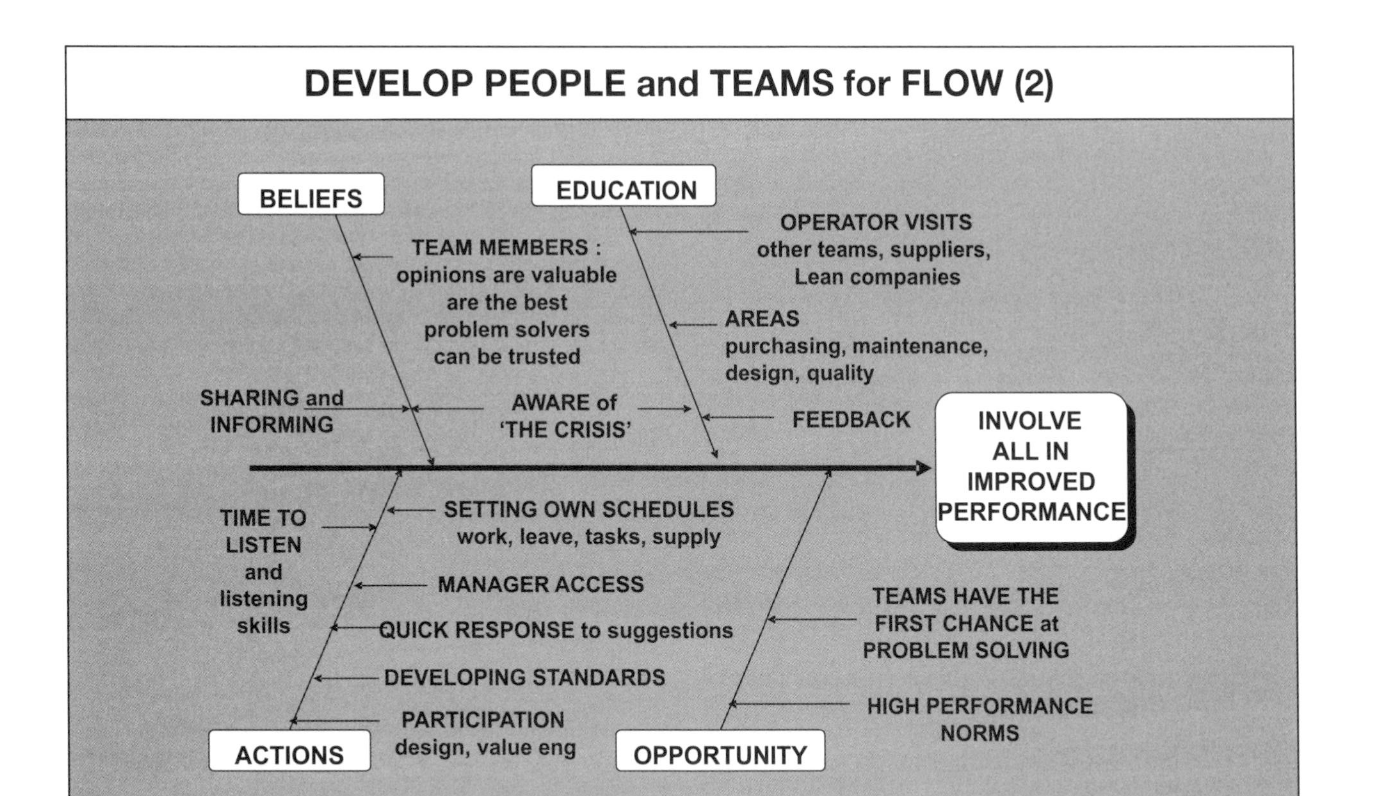
DEVELOP PEOPLE and TEAMS for FLOW (2)
BELIEFS
TEAM MEMBERS : opinions are valuable are the best problem solvers can be trusted
SHARING and INFORMING
AWARE of 'THE CRISIS'
EDUCATION
OPERATOR VISITS other teams, suppliers, Lean companies
AREAS purchasing, maintenance, design, quality
FEEDBACK
INVOLVE ALL IN IMPROVED PERFORMANCE
TIME TO LISTEN and listening skills
SETTING OWN SCHEDULES work, leave, tasks, supply
MANAGER ACCESS
QUICK RESPONSE to suggestions
DEVELOPING STANDARDS
PARTICIPATION design, value eng
ACTIONS
OPPORTUNITY
TEAMS HAVE THE FIRST CHANCE at PROBLEM SOLVING
HIGH PERFORMANCE NORMS

Team Involvement

Having developed the people and team (shown in the first figure), they are then involved in achieving high performance. Of course, this is also an ongoing process.

Beliefs

The underlying belief is that those close to the action are best qualified to make improvements, they are good problem solvers (at least with coaching) and can be trusted to lead the attack on waste. This implies a new role for "experts" such as industrial engineers, maintenance engineers, and quality professionals who become facilitators and coaches rather than front line improvers. The experts need to be good listeners because operators have valuable opinions.

Actions

Increasingly self directed teams are taking over tasks such as scheduling, work allocation, leave, hiring, purchasing, even rewards. Teams can communicate horizontally whilst notifying management ("U") rather than having to work up and down the organisational hierarchy ("H"). Shopfloor team members are also useful in design and value engineering studies, to improve manufacturability.

It usually takes two years for a team to evolve into full self-directed status, and in the early years there may well be a drop in productivity as the team finds its feet. But in many companies the rewards of self-direction are great: improved quality and productivity, reduced staff turnover, increased flexibility – in short a flatter and leaner organisation.

Open Book Management is a growing concept whereby information on both the "financials" and operations is given to operators, in whole or in part, to help them make better suggestions. It is also about involvement, belief, and trust.

Opportunity

Teams must have the first chance to make improvements themselves, before "experts" step in. This fosters ownership. Undercapacity scheduling deliberately allows time for improvement, and offsets the squeezing out of thinking by output pressure. All this should work in an atmosphere of high performance norms, where teams are expected to perform well and to improve. Expectation breeds results – the "Pygmalion" effect is proven.

Education

Team members should assist in educating both themselves and other members. Visits to other teams, good lean companies, and to suppliers and customers builds understanding and motivation and helps cut waste. Education should be "just in time" – application immediately following instruction.

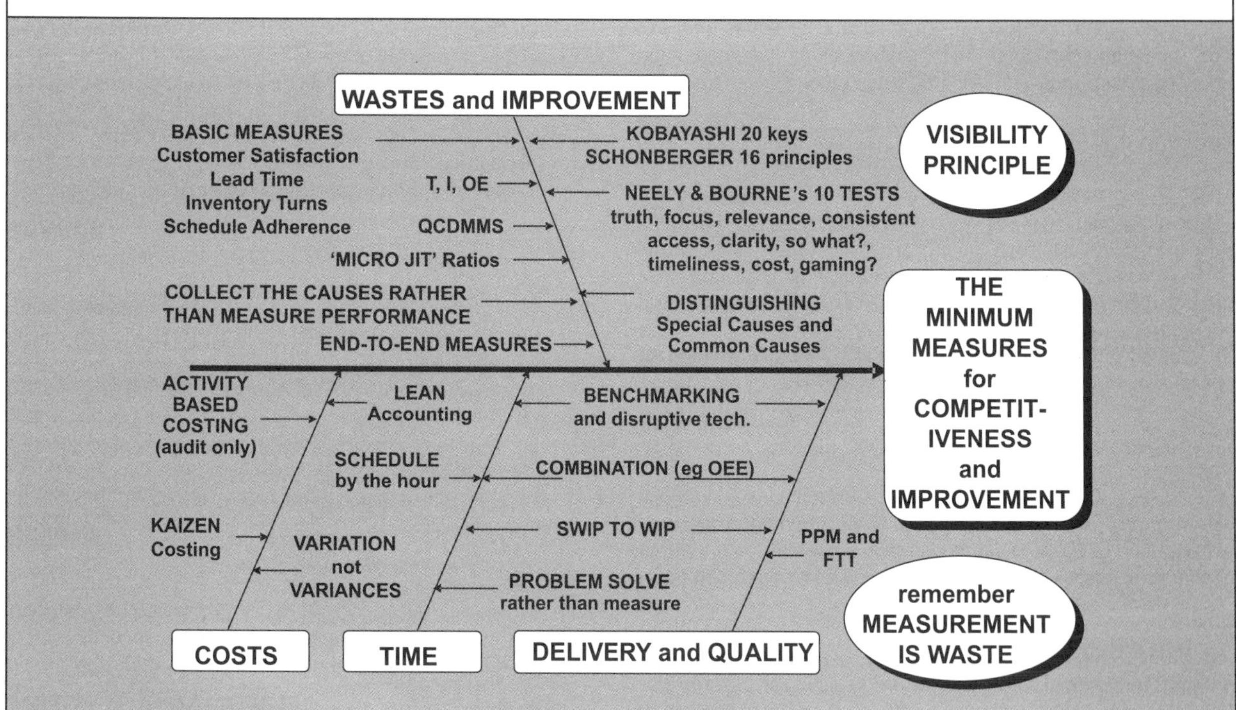
MEASURING for Flow
WASTES and IMPROVEMENT
BASIC MEASURES
Customer Satisfaction
Lead Time
Inventory Turns
Schedule Adherence
T, I, OE
QCDMMS
'MICRO JIT' Ratios
COLLECT THE CAUSES RATHER
THAN MEASURE PERFORMANCE
END-TO-END MEASURES
KOBAYASHI 20 keys
SCHONBERGER 16 principles
NEELY & BOURNE's 10 TESTS
truth, focus, relevance, consistent
access, clarity, so what?,
timeliness, cost, gaming?
DISTINGUISHING
Special Causes and
Common Causes
VISIBILITY
PRINCIPLE
THE
MINIMUM
MEASURES
for
COMPETIT-
IVENESS
and
IMPROVEMENT
ACTIVITY
BASED
COSTING
(audit only)
LEAN
Accounting
BENCHMARKING
and disruptive tech.
SCHEDULE
by the hour
COMBINATION (eg OEE)
KAIZEN
Costing
VARIATION
not
VARIANCES
SWIP TO WIP
PPM and
FTT
PROBLEM SOLVE
rather than measure
COSTS
TIME
DELIVERY and QUALITY
remember
MEASUREMENT
IS WASTE

MEASURE for Flow

Measurement is a necessary waste with lean and supply chain, so the minimum necessary actions should be sought. Measurement should be set and taken with the participation of those being measured. Measures should be at the appropriate level (where something can be done about it). And measures should be made visible and kept at "gemba".

Concepts and Improvement

The basic four measures in lean are customer satisfaction, lead time, quality performance, and schedule adherence. Cost and inventory turns are close seconds, but result from the first four. QCDMMS is frequently found in lean plants: quality, cost, delivery, management, morale, and safety. Management means a measure on participation and involvement.

Think of developing measures in two ways. One is via policy deployment: measures should filter down, level by level, reflecting higher level projects and priorities. A second is developing measures first at the cell or point level, then at the internal value stream level, then at the full value stream level, and then at the organizational or strategic level. Brian Maskell, in *Practical Lean Accounting*, suggests measures at each , for example OEE, first time through, WIP to SWIP, and day-by-the-hour measures at the cell level, dock-to-dock time and average cost per unit at the value stream level, and customer satisfaction, inventory days, and sales growth at the strategic level.

Deming (and Six Sigma) reminds us that all measures are subject to variation, so distinguish common causes from special causes. Don't waste time on explaining common cause variation.

Neely and Bourne suggest 10 tests: truth (measuring what it is supposed to measure), focus, relevance, consistency, access, clarity, so what?, timeliness, cost, and gaming possibilities.

Goldratt goes for throughput or flow, inventory and operating expense. Throughput does not become throughput unless it is sold. Inventory should be primarily WIP, rather than raw material and finished goods over which the manager has less than full control. And operating expenses are all the costs, direct and indirect, needed to convert inventory into throughput.

Self-audit measures are useful. Kobayashi's 20 keys allow self-rating in 20 shop floor oriented areas, on a 1 to 5 scale. Schonberger's 16 Principles are an alternative applicable throughout the enterprise and supply chain. In related work, Schonberger talks about three levels of measures. The first are those (such as quality, delivery, and changeover) that can be influenced on a day to day basis and should be measured on a day to day basis. At the next level are measures that result from performance in these day to day activities. Complaints are an example. These, like SPC, should not be tampered in the short term except when special causes are apparent. And on yet a higher level measures such as inventory turns and costs are even more indirect and should be regarded as the outcome of lower level actions, and not set directly. Statistical thinking means measuring variation.

LEAN ACCOUNTING for Flow

COSTING
- DIRECT COSTS
- ACTIVITY-BASED audit only
- 'KAIZEN COSTING'
- REMAINING O/HEADS ALLOCATED BY LEAD TIME
- REDUCE OVERHEAD STRUCTURE
- EXPLAIN VARIATION NOT VARIANCES (special causes only)

SIMPLICITY and REPORTING
- PRIME MEASURES NON-FINANCIAL
- "95% BETTER THAN 100%"
- END TO END measures
- VISUAL REPORTING graphs, control charts, traffic lights

TRANSACTIONS and INVENTORY
- 5S ON TRANSACTIONS
- REDUCE RECONCILIATION
- REDUCE FGI
- CYCLE COUNT OF WIP
- TRACKING BY VISUAL MANAGEMENT Inventory, supply
- PAYMENT BY BACKFLUSH

ORGANIZATION
- ACCOUNTING AS SERVANTS TO OPS
- OPEN BOOK bias
- DECENTRALISED
- ORGANISED BY VALUE STREAM direct association

ACCOUNTING with SPEED, SIMPLICITY, and LEAN SUPPORT

LEAN ACCOUNTING for Flow

Lean Accounting is increasingly relevant as the realisation dawns that accounting is not only a source of huge waste and unnecessary overhead, but can also lead the lean enterprise inadvertently in the wrong direction.

Costing

One problem has been overhead allocation which frequently leads to undercosting poor products and overcosting others, and occasionally leads to closing whole plants or moving operations overseas. A start is to try to have all costs directly associated with a value stream. This requires layout and value stream change, not just accounting change. Have a programme which steadily reduces overhead structure and associates overheads directly with value streams. Remaining overheads are allocated perhaps by lead time, not labour hours. Activity based costing is another possibility, but at a penalty of complexity. Kaizen costing is not really costing but monitoring actual performance against targets with costing only being done when there is a major change. And only special cause variation needs to be explained. Eliminate variances.

Simplicity and Organization

Accounting is there to support operations and help with decisions and so should place minimum burden on operations. The prime measures are operations, not financial. They should be graphically displayed for trend and variation; individual figures are meaningless. Traffic lights help. '95% is better than 100% means that 95% measures given quickly are far better than 100% correct given weeks late.'

Consider to what extent the books can be opened to different levels. Opening the books means having clear, simple financial statements that anyone can read. Don't train others to read financial statements; train the accountants to give out meaningful easy-to-interpret statements that help decision making.

Transactions

Reducing transactions must be an ongoing activity in any lean organization. So many need to be questioned. Do a 5S. Do a 5 Whys. Alongside this, seek to reduce and streamline the reconciliation procedures. Pay as many accounts as possible automatically by backflush procedures.
On inventory lean should lead to huge simplification of inventory counts – via kanban and standard containers.

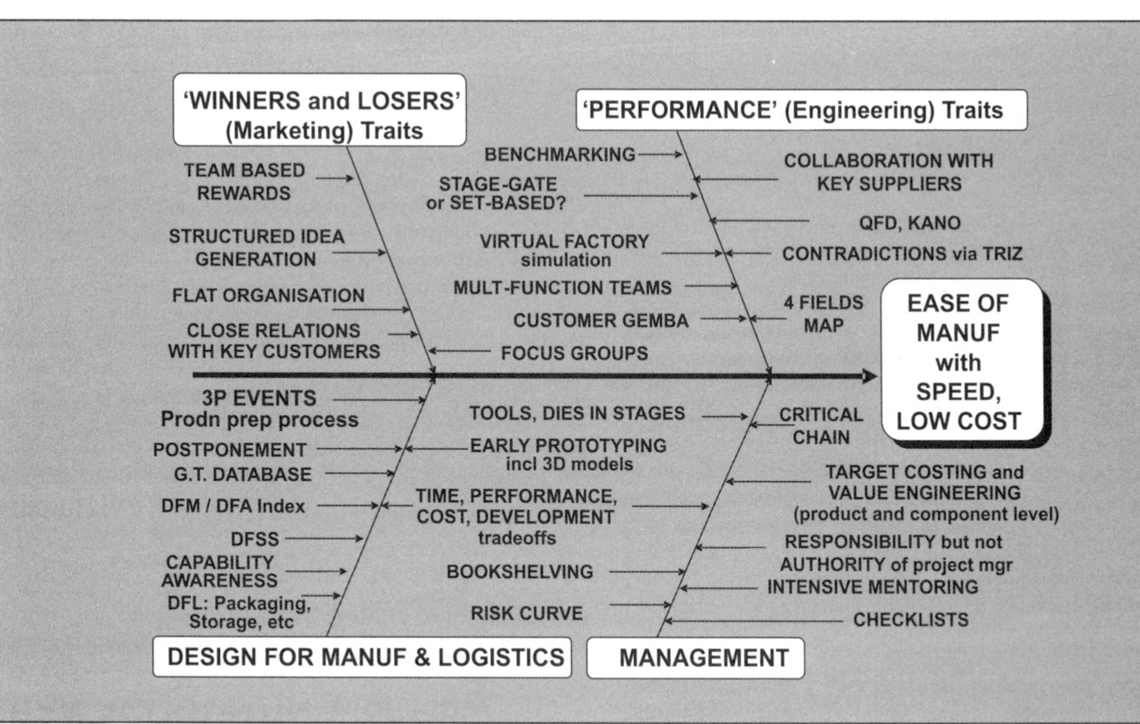
DESIGN and NPD for Flow
'WINNERS and LOSERS' (Marketing) Traits
TEAM BASED REWARDS
STRUCTURED IDEA GENERATION
FLAT ORGANISATION
CLOSE RELATIONS WITH KEY CUSTOMERS
'PERFORMANCE' (Engineering) Traits
BENCHMARKING
STAGE-GATE or SET-BASED?
VIRTUAL FACTORY simulation
MULT-FUNCTION TEAMS
CUSTOMER GEMBA
FOCUS GROUPS
COLLABORATION WITH KEY SUPPLIERS
QFD, KANO
CONTRADICTIONS via TRIZ
4 FIELDS MAP
EASE OF MANUF with SPEED, LOW COST
3P EVENTS
Prodn prep process
POSTPONEMENT
G.T. DATABASE
DFM / DFA Index
DFSS
CAPABILITY AWARENESS
DFL: Packaging, Storage, etc
DESIGN FOR MANUF & LOGISTICS
TOOLS, DIES IN STAGES
EARLY PROTOTYPING incl 3D models
TIME, PERFORMANCE, COST, DEVELOPMENT tradeoffs
BOOKSHELVING
RISK CURVE
CRITICAL CHAIN
TARGET COSTING and VALUE ENGINEERING (product and component level)
RESPONSIBILITY but not AUTHORITY of project mgr
INTENSIVE MENTORING
CHECKLISTS
MANAGEMENT

DESIGN and New Product Development for Flow

It is said that 80% of costs become locked in at the design stage. But that is only a part of the picture. Design is the major factor in many product sales. Time to market, an increasingly important feature of competitiveness is strongly influenced by the design stage. This is a summary of what can be done.

Management

The Lean or Toyota approach to design is different. Some characteristics follow: The project manager concerned with a new product is a respected engineer who manages by influence and respect rather than a manager who controls via deadlines. He has responsibility but not authority. He would have a small central team, but works through the line managers. Deadlines or milestones are few, but absolute. Line managers have responsibility for researching and developing their own particular technologies. This leads to the 'set-based' approach whereby the design begins with several options for each major subassembly, and these are gradually narrowed. So it is a postponement approach. Rejected alternatives are not scrapped, but 'bookshelved' for subsequent use. Line managers give intensive monitoring to younger designers, using PDCA. Note books record and accumulate the lessons learned in each design. These form the checklist for next time, and accumulate into hugely valuable documents. Target costing and value engineering are extensively used. The project manager monitors progress by a 'critical chain' (Goldratt) rather than critical patch approach. The latter seeks not to delay progress by avoiding resource conflicts. Tools, dies, machines, and specifications are developed in stages, first broad, then narrower.

See the fishbone on Project Flow.

Mapping the design and NPD process can be a revelation

Many designers begin design by consulting a group technology or similar database. They are looking for similar products and components. They also wish to use standard parts to minimise inventory proliferation. Value engineering, either to improve value at same cost or reduce cost while retaining characteristics, is a team activity done before manufacture. VE uses functional analysis to identify the basic functions and then uses creative thinking to simplify. Standardisation weighs the cost of providing a feature to all products against the complexity costs of inventory and scheduling by providing it as an option.

Going to "gemba" is desirable. For example sending the concept team to live in the customer market for three months, as with Lexus, or speaking directly to customers.

Platforms have emerged as a major concept in automotive, now extending to other products. Two calculators may look different but underlying they share the same platform and a majority of

components. Mass Customisation attempts to gain the advantages of the assembly line but for customised products. This is done by modularity, postponement, late packaging, re-sequencing (e.g. Benetton dying jerseys after not before manufacture), point of sale configuration (Dell computer), or several of these.

The effectiveness of design for manufacture (DFA) and design for assembly (DFA) may be measured by an index developed by Boothroyd and Dewhurst. In the design process four important variables are time, product performance, product cost, and development. The interconnections represent six tradeoffs that should be explicitly made (Smith and Reinertson). Quality Function Deployment (QFD) is a major technique for design and development teams, which systematically integrates the "voice of the customer", benchmarking, comparative products, and product features. Design for Logistics can lead to big savings by incorporating packaging, storage, vehicle compatibility, and recycling considerations for conditions to be encountered along the distribution chain.

Working with suppliers on product design is increasing. This uses early consultation with suppliers having focused expertise and who may be responsible for whole "corners", not just parts. The "open spec" concept aids this by giving suppliers the minimum possible spec to allow maximum innovation. Bookshelving is where co-operation with a supplier leads to technical advance that is stored for future use but which can be incorporated very quickly.

Marketing and Engineering Traits

Cardiff research (Mark Francis) has identified the traits of more successful lean design organizations. The marketing and engineering traits, or commonly used tools and approaches, are given in the figure.

SERVICE, ADMINISTRATION and OFFICE

Today manufacturing and service are bundled. Moreover, as flow improves on the shop floor, shortcomings in the office become more apparent. For both these reasons service and administration need attention. This is discussed in the next three figures.

Flow SERVICE and ADMINISTRATION

Understanding Demand

The starting point is an understanding of demand. John Seddon has given the important concept of *value demand*, first time demand, the basic requirements of customers, and *failure demand* as a result of not doing something correctly the first time or at all, leading to repeat calls. Failure demand should be identified and eliminated. Sometimes when this is done, unexpected resources are freed up, quality, lead time and satisfaction improve dramatically.

Having separated failure demand, variation in demand must be appreciated. Service always requires excess capacity, but how much depends on both expectation of response and demand variation.

System

Service is a system, requiring a total system or holistic response. It is the people, the machines, the information all working together. Small things can upset systems or customers. Systems have feedback – negative word of mouth, but also a loop where employees and facilities drive service which drives satisfaction, which drives retention, which drives profit, which enables better and better trained employees and facilities. Deming said 94% of problems were due to the system, only 6% due to the people. Only management can fix the system. Is the service system in control? Plot the demand variation and service response against time and find out. If yes, go onto the gaps below. If no, there must be some special causes at work in the wider system. Identify when, where, how, who. Is the data dirty? In other words is it not correct, in full, right first time? In the system there are 4 gaps (Ziethaml) that lead to the overall gap in customer satisfaction – the gap between customer expectations and the perception of the expectation, between the perception and the standards or specification, between the specification and delivery, and between actual delivery and communication about delivery that conditions expectations. Identify and narrow the gaps.

Wastes and Improvement

Like other areas, proceed via the PDCA cycle. Learn. Be aware of the seven service wastes. (See separate figure.) Variation can be reduced by applying the 7 tools of quality and/or six sigma concepts. (See separate figure.) Standard operations are a good tool for improving service and reducing variation, but do not try to standardise failure demand or special cause variations.

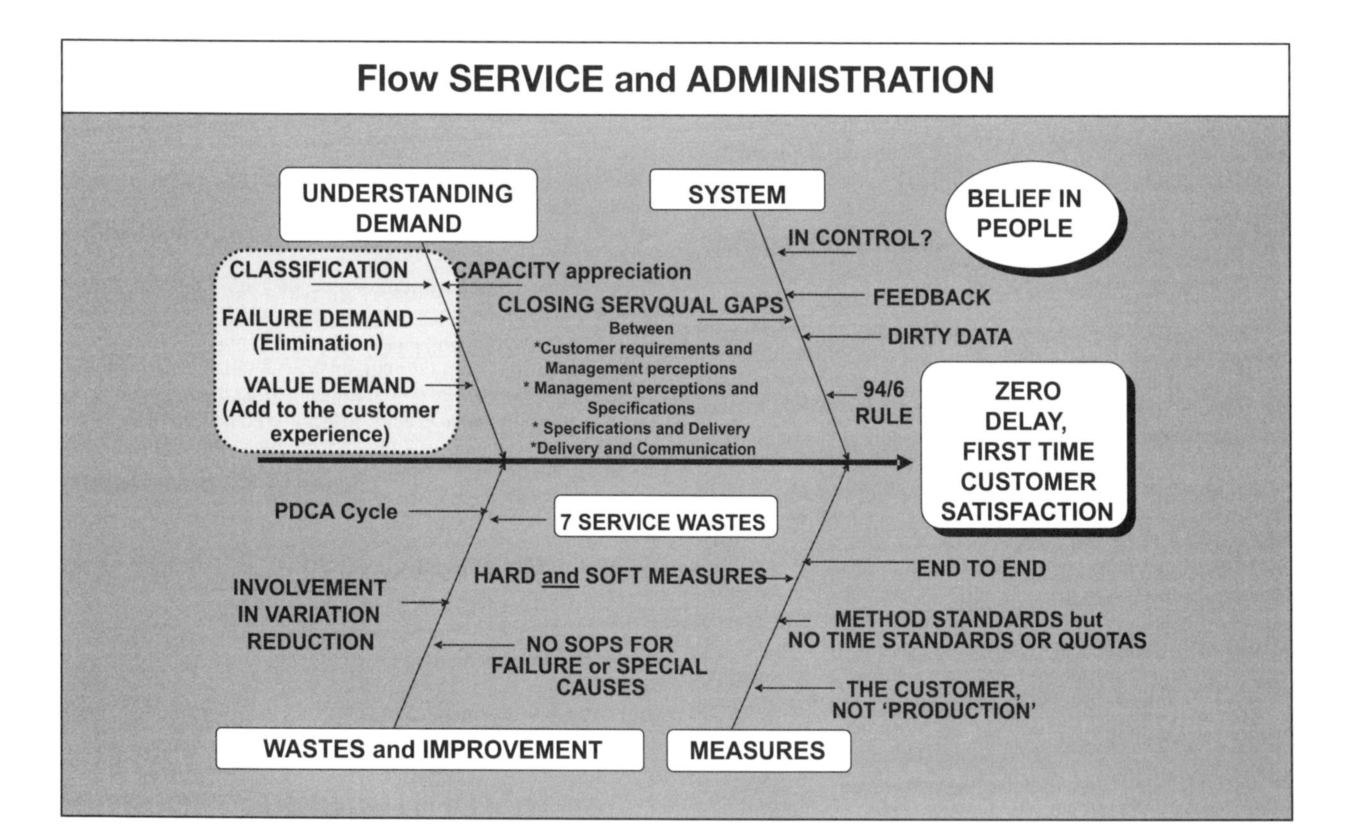
Flow SERVICE and ADMINISTRATION
UNDERSTANDING DEMAND
CLASSIFICATION
FAILURE DEMAND (Elimination)
VALUE DEMAND (Add to the customer experience)
CAPACITY appreciation
CLOSING SERVQUAL GAPS
Between
*Customer requirements and Management perceptions
* Management perceptions and Specifications
* Specifications and Delivery
*Delivery and Communication
SYSTEM
IN CONTROL?
FEEDBACK
DIRTY DATA
94/6 RULE
BELIEF IN PEOPLE
ZERO DELAY, FIRST TIME CUSTOMER SATISFACTION
PDCA Cycle
7 SERVICE WASTES
INVOLVEMENT IN VARIATION REDUCTION
HARD and SOFT MEASURES
NO SOPS FOR FAILURE or SPECIAL CAUSES
END TO END
METHOD STANDARDS but NO TIME STANDARDS OR QUOTAS
THE CUSTOMER, NOT 'PRODUCTION'
WASTES and IMPROVEMENT
MEASURES

Measures

First, focus on what is important to the customer, not what is important to managers or operations. Service measures must be end-to-end, not functional. Beware of quotas (for example number of calls per hour) that can have a devastating effect on service.

Flow in the OFFICE

The office deserves special attention – the 'cell' of administration.

Visibility

5S and visibility principles (see separate figures) are equally applicable. Display daily and monthly performance, and activities. This requires thinking out what the daily and monthly activities are, then showing and tracking them. These could be invoices processed, financial reconciliations, reports produced. Also put on display what people are doing and what progress is being made – gantt charts, people activities, projects against milestones. Open plan offices with common meeting areas encourage cross functional talk.

Layout

Some sequential activities in offices could benefit from cell and one-piece flow principles – or 'pulse lines' using longer cycles and standard work. (See layout figure.) In any case batching must be reduced. Can processes be combined or, better still made one-stop for customers? Kaizen works also: have flip charts to collect and pareto problems. Why not hold Kaizen events in the office?

Service and Flow

As with manufacturing, *learning to see* mapping is powerful in administrative areas, especially with repetitive work sequences. Here the emphasis is on cutting waste and reducing lead time. In customer-facing situations, the cycle of service or service blueprint is more suitable. Here the emphasis is on improving the customer experience. Use the Kano model on every 'Moment of Truth'. (See customer service figure.)

The service wastes will be useful. Hammer's BPR principles are useful for office flow. These include doing operations in parallel, seeking one-stop solutions, minimising reconciliation, workers making decisions where possible, reducing batches, never delaying value adding by non value adding, and having different processing streams for different customer types. Remember Hammer's famous statement – 'don't automate, obliterate'; don't automate waste.

People

As with manufacturing cells, office cells work better when made autonomous and held accountable. Encourage people to report and display progress, day by day. And use critical chain methods. (See Project flow figure.)

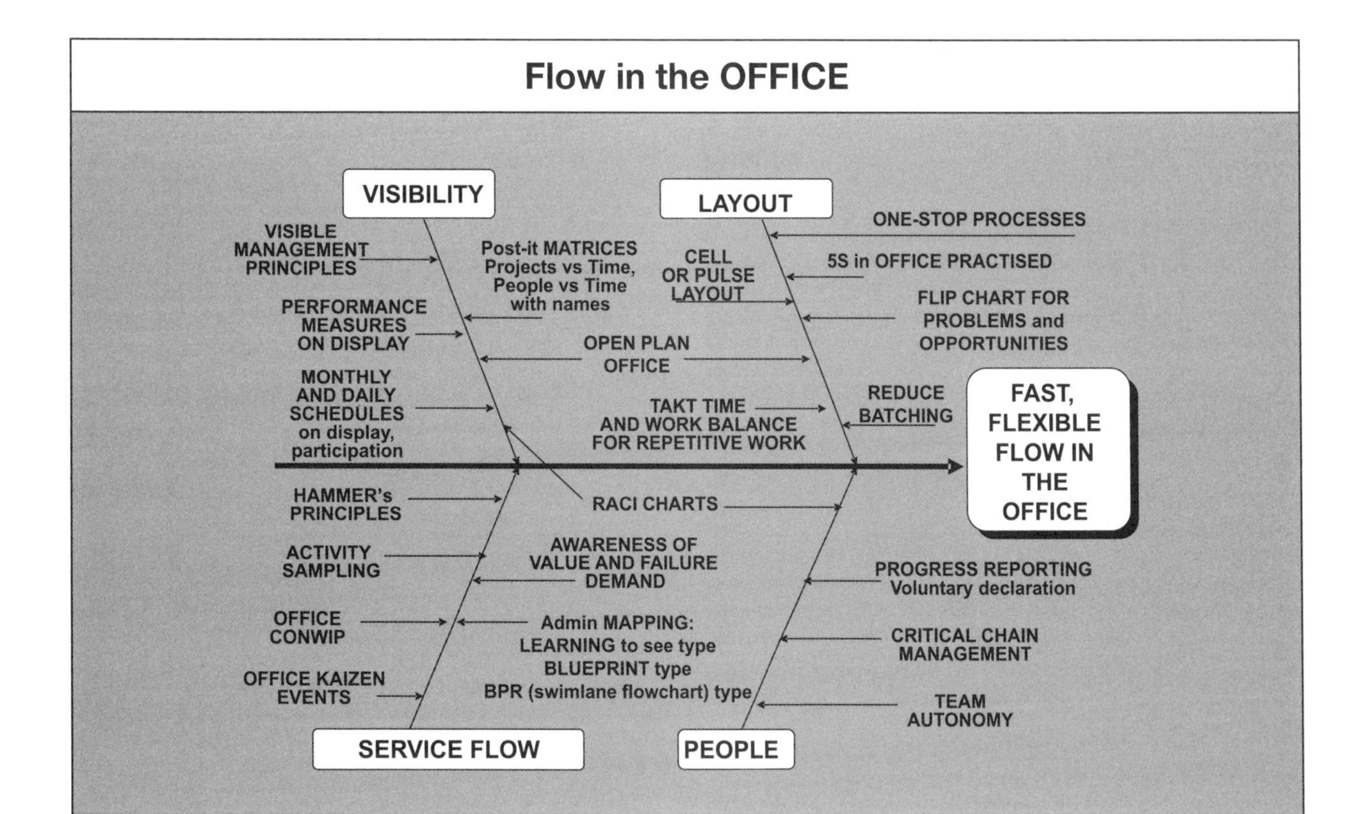
Flow in the OFFICE
VISIBILITY
LAYOUT
VISIBLE MANAGEMENT PRINCIPLES
Post-it MATRICES Projects vs Time, People vs Time with names
CELL OR PULSE LAYOUT
ONE-STOP PROCESSES
5S in OFFICE PRACTISED
PERFORMANCE MEASURES ON DISPLAY
FLIP CHART FOR PROBLEMS and OPPORTUNITIES
OPEN PLAN OFFICE
MONTHLY AND DAILY SCHEDULES on display, participation
TAKT TIME AND WORK BALANCE FOR REPETITIVE WORK
REDUCE BATCHING
FAST, FLEXIBLE FLOW IN THE OFFICE
HAMMER's PRINCIPLES
RACI CHARTS
ACTIVITY SAMPLING
AWARENESS OF VALUE AND FAILURE DEMAND
PROGRESS REPORTING Voluntary declaration
OFFICE CONWIP
Admin MAPPING: LEARNING to see type BLUEPRINT type BPR (swimlane flowchart) type
CRITICAL CHAIN MANAGEMENT
OFFICE KAIZEN EVENTS
TEAM AUTONOMY
SERVICE FLOW
PEOPLE

CUSTOMER SERVICE for Flow

There are two aspects: winning customers and retaining them. It is one supply chain and its product-service package against another, rather than one manufacturer and its products against another. And everyone is involved.

Winning Customers

Winning customers involves, first and foremost, understanding customer value. Value is product and service benefit divided by cost. "You don't sell customers a product but a benefit" is an old marketing idea but valued benefits are hard to identify. One way is surely to extend the lean principles of visibility, of gemba, of involvement, of partnership and passing on the benefits, of clear communication, out to customers. And who is a customer? Final, intermediate, supply chain, or all?

Winning customers by word of mouth may involve "memorable experiences"; mere satisfaction is no longer good enough. Exceeding expectations – what Kano refers to as "delighters" – is something to strive for, but for lean, six sigma and supply chain, delivering superior results on the performance factors is as important. Customers ultimately seek 'free, perfect, and now' – move in this direction.

One way is to map the sequence of customer interface activities or "moments of truth", and for each to ensure that (a) "basics" are met (b) performance is superior (c) delighters or WOW! factors are provided whenever economically possible (d) standards and consistency are adhered to, and (e) where possible actions are failsafed or error proofed. So instead of looking for value add and non value add activities as would be done internally, interpret the word "value" in wider terms from the customer perspective. Note that the sequence of activities begins with the customer thinking about buying and only ends when the product is finally disposed of.

Another way is to pass on the time benefits of lean and supply chain, in other words to reduce lead times and allow customers to cut their own inventories and become more agile. This strengthens the supply chain.

The "Service Profit Chain" is a phrase coined by Sasser at Harvard to illustrate the systems thinking nature of good service. Good company policies towards employees result in motivated employees. Motivated employees, together with supportive service policies allow good service to be delivered. Good service delivery results in customer satisfaction. Customer satisfaction results in repeat business. Repeated business means more profit to support good employee policies. The 3 R's of service are retention, referrals, and related products that together form a powerful feedback loop.

Retaining Customers

Today the benefits of retaining customers are better understood. "It costs five times as much to win a new customer as it does to retain an existing one", and "benefits of retained customers continue to accrue with minimal promotion year after year". So reward

CUSTOMER SERVICE for Flow

WINNING CUSTOMERS

- UNDERSTANDING WHAT CUSTOMERS VALUE
  Kano Model, Gemba Listening
- SWIFT EVEN FLOW
- CYCLE OF SERVICE, moments of truth
- EXCEED EXPECTATIONS
- AWARENESS OF 7 SERVICE WASTES

RETAINING CUSTOMERS

- REWARD REPEAT CUSTOM
- IMPROVE SERVICE DELIVERY
- MAKING IT EASY to order, to complain
- SERVICE RECOVERY PLANS
- UNDER PROMISE, OVER DELIVER
- "SERVICE PROFIT CHAIN"
  retention, referrals,
  related products

FOLLOW THROUGH Lean TO CUSTOMERS

FEEDBACK TO DESIGN AND OPERATIONS

repeat custom by sharing the benefits. Good service delivery means closing the gaps, as described by Zeithaml in "Delivering Quality Service", between (a) expected service perceptions of customer expectations (b) perceptions of customer expectations and service specifications (c) service specifications and service delivery, and (d) service delivery and communications about the service. This of course implies measuring the extent of each gap. A good policy is to under-promise on delivery time, product performance, and service backup and over-deliver rather than the reverse.

Because some things are still bound to go wrong, despite standardisation and failsafeing, have a good service recovery plan prepared in advance. Research has shown that excellent service recovery not only retains custom, but also builds loyalty. The aim is not only to restore confidence, but also to limit the possibility of it happening again. It's continuous improvement.

Measure service performance, not mere satisfaction. For example a supermarket measure is having the correct product (no substitutes), in the required quantity, when needed.

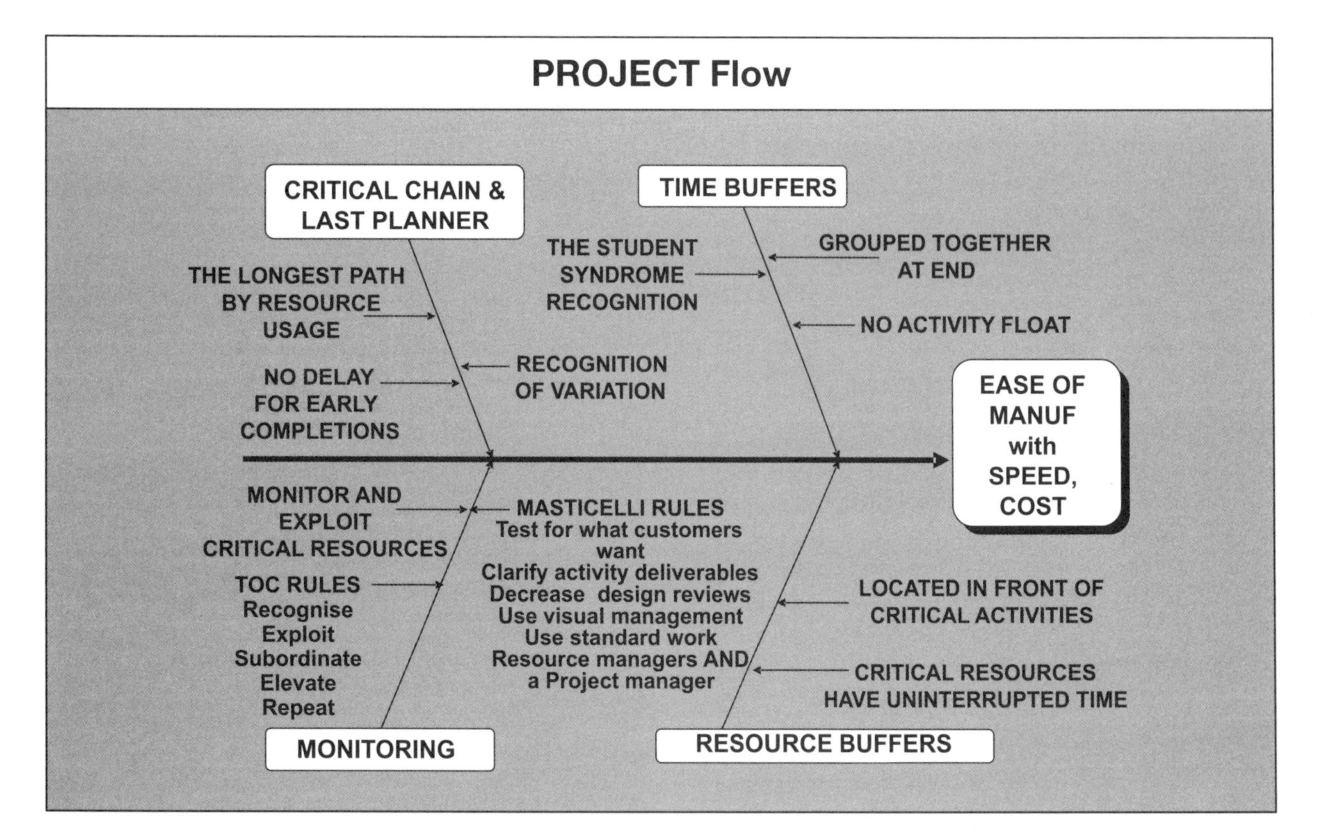
PROJECT Flow
CRITICAL CHAIN & LAST PLANNER
THE LONGEST PATH BY RESOURCE USAGE
NO DELAY FOR EARLY COMPLETIONS
RECOGNITION OF VARIATION
TIME BUFFERS
THE STUDENT SYNDROME RECOGNITION
GROUPED TOGETHER AT END
NO ACTIVITY FLOAT
EASE OF MANUF with SPEED, COST
MONITOR AND EXPLOIT CRITICAL RESOURCES
TOC RULES
Recognise
Exploit
Subordinate
Elevate
Repeat
MASTICELLI RULES
Test for what customers want
Clarify activity deliverables
Decrease design reviews
Use visual management
Use standard work
Resource managers AND a Project manager
LOCATED IN FRONT OF CRITICAL ACTIVITIES
CRITICAL RESOURCES HAVE UNINTERRUPTED TIME
MONITORING
RESOURCE BUFFERS

PROJECT Flow

Projects are everywhere in Lean: in new products, in strategy and change, in moves, in maintenance. And then there is Lean construction....

Critical Chain and Last Planner

Yes, the critical path (the longest route) is important, but even more so is the longest path by resource usage. If a resource is required on two activities, only one can be done at a time. Determine the critical resources. Then ensure that once started, resource critical activities are uninterrupted. The Last Planner is a method that tries to identify all possible delays for each job before it is due. This is a learning process.

If work is completed early on resource critical, there should be no delay in starting the next task. This means planning to finish activities early that otherwise could delay resource critical activities.

Time Buffers and Resource Buffers

Like Drum Buffer Rope, time buffers are important. Accumulate all safety time at the end of the project, not spread throughout. Don't do the 'student syndrome' taking all buffer time up-front. Ensure that resource critical activities are not delayed. This may mean a buffer of reserve work, and monitoring activities that lead onto resource critical activities.

Monitoring

Monitor the resource critical activities, use the TOC rules. (See Managing the Constraint fishbone.)

The 'Masticelli Rules' are useful: test for what customers actually want: cost, time, quality etc. Clarify the deliverables. Decrease design or progress reviews; they are mainly waste. Use standard work where possible. Have a project manager AND resource managers for critical resources.

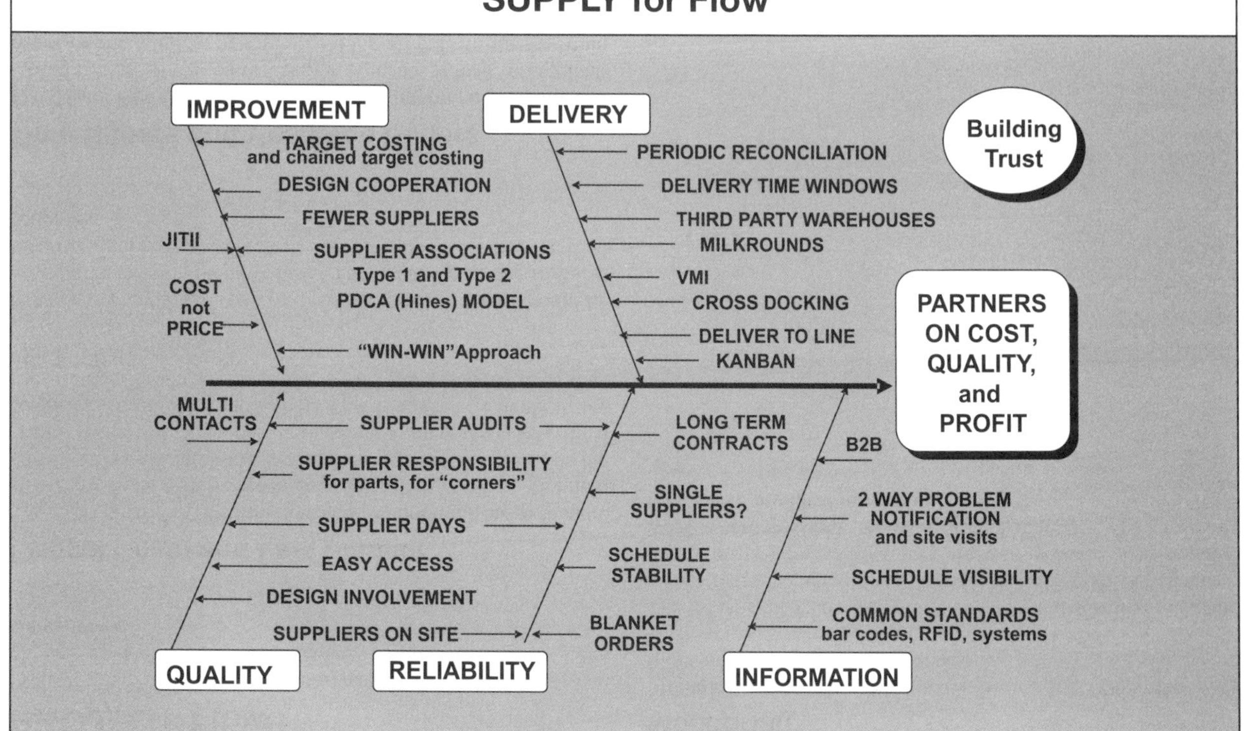
SUPPLY for Flow
IMPROVEMENT
TARGET COSTING
and chained target costing
DESIGN COOPERATION
FEWER SUPPLIERS
JITII
SUPPLIER ASSOCIATIONS
Type 1 and Type 2
PDCA (Hines) MODEL
COST
not
PRICE
"WIN-WIN" Approach
DELIVERY
PERIODIC RECONCILIATION
DELIVERY TIME WINDOWS
THIRD PARTY WAREHOUSES
MILKROUNDS
VMI
CROSS DOCKING
DELIVER TO LINE
KANBAN
Building
Trust
PARTNERS
ON COST,
QUALITY,
and
PROFIT
MULTI
CONTACTS
SUPPLIER AUDITS
SUPPLIER RESPONSIBILITY
for parts, for "corners"
SUPPLIER DAYS
EASY ACCESS
DESIGN INVOLVEMENT
SUPPLIERS ON SITE
QUALITY
LONG TERM
CONTRACTS
SINGLE
SUPPLIERS?
SCHEDULE
STABILITY
BLANKET
ORDERS
RELIABILITY
B2B
2 WAY PROBLEM
NOTIFICATION
and site visits
SCHEDULE VISIBILITY
COMMON STANDARDS
bar codes, RFID, systems
INFORMATION

SUPPLY for Flow

The Supply Chain emerged as a major force for competitiveness during the 1990s, but supplier partnership is much older. Most companies have supply chains and distribution chains. These work together with internal processes. Improving cost, quality, delivery and service is what supply chain co-operation is all about. This requires that all members of the chain, end to end, supply to distribution, adopt lean principles, six sigma principles and supply chain principles. Of course this is a long task.

The marriage analogy is appropriate. Marriage is for the longer term. It is based on trust and mutual respect. It will have its ups and downs, but with give and take both are better off. Marriage involves commitment to a single partner, not playing the field.

Improvement and Cost

The first principle is buying on cost not price. Cost is a far wider concept including quality, reliability, and delivery. Supply cost reduction has several strands. Target costing, used often with value engineering, has both internal and supplier implications. Target cost = market price – profit. This leads to the "allowable cost" for products and components. Achieving component costs is a target for suppliers, who are assisted by company personnel. Several methods discussed in the Design section are relevant. Target costing may extend to "chained target costing" whereby various tiers in a supply chain co-operate to achieve target costs at their own respective levels. There may be several of these chains, and the exercise may begin half way down a chain, not necessarily at the final product stage.

Design co-operation calls for suppliers to participate in, or take over, design for which they have particular expertise. With trust, wastes between the partners can be identified and eliminated. Examples include double buffers, inspection, billing. The ideal is delivery to the point of use, under pull, with perfect quality. Waste reduction is achieved by sharing expertise, and joint teams, on all topics in this book. This is "win-win" for both parties – security, confidence to invest, and low cost. Risk is reduced because there is too much to lose. Of course, this is only possible with fewer suppliers, so a process of selecting partners must begin. Holding "supplier days" to explain expectations should be periodic. For some, JITII is a possibility whereby premier supplier's representatives work at the company site writing purchase orders on their own company and co-operating with product development.

Supplier Associations, or clubs, can help. Type1 is a group of suppliers selected by a customer. Benchmarking is done and sharing expertise begins. A problem may be that ***no-one*** in the group is world class, so it is essentially catch-up. Type 2 is also assembled by a customer, but here the customer company plays an active role in mapping out and assisting with development. Sharing and cooperation still take place. This is harder to establish, but more focused.

Peter Hines' 10 step PDCA supplier association model has the stages of benchmark competitive position, select appropriate development tools, gain internal acceptance, select suppliers to participate, benchmark supplier position, jointly target improvements, focus development and coordination effort, undertake group activities, measure improvements, and refocus and redefine target areas.

Quality

Ideally suppliers should deliver perfect quality direct to the point of use without the necessity for inspection. Historically only purchasing spoke to purchasing; now there are multiple points of contact: quality to quality, scheduling to scheduling, design to design. Increasingly suppliers are asked to take over responsibility for larger assemblies (or 'corners') not just components. Quality is a prime reason, but cost, expertise, and control are other reasons. At some automotive plants this extends to having suppliers' employees actually doing the assembly on the final product site. Improving quality involves working more closely with supplier designers, not only first tier. Easy access to design and process information encourages trust, reduces cost, and improves awareness of requirements. Supplier Associations have become a major means of fostering improved supplier performance. These are "clubs", often sponsored by a major customer, which co-operate by sharing expertise and resources and solving mutual problems. Other types co-operate within a region.

Reliability

Quality and delivery reliability is frequently measured by a rating scheme. Poor suppliers get dropped; good suppliers win more business and long term contracts. Such contracts, combined with single or few suppliers encourage good performance. One practice is to develop two good suppliers for a major component and then to award one of them life-of-the-product business. Another product may see the second supplier winning. Schedule stability is encouraged by demand management practices (see Align Demand figure) and blanket orders.

Delivery

The lean delivery ideal is direct to the line via kanban pull in small batches. Milkrounds, delivering several components in small batches instead of one component in a larger batch, makes this economic. Fewer suppliers, supplying more parts also helps to make this cost effective. Delivery is within specific time windows, and periodic reconciliation or even self-billing rather than invoicing cuts costs. A third party warehouse or in-house supermarket, from where parts are delivered to the line in small batches, but received in larger batches may be in interim solution.

Vendor managed inventory (VMI) is increasingly used for C class commodities, particularly runner and repeater items.

Wal-Mart has continued to demonstrate the effectiveness of cross-docking where inventory is transferred between stages in the supply chain in hours, rather than spending weeks in a warehouse. Close coordination and timing are required.

Information

Is the glue that welds suppliers. Schedule visibility is a goal, sometimes electronic through the web. Common standards on RFID, bar codes, computer systems, and containers help. So does two-way problem notification whereby each side gives maximum warning of any disruption. Site visits by all manner of personnel, from operator to CEO, assist understanding and can cut duplication wastes.

DISTRIBUTE for Flow

FLOW and INVENTORY

POSTPONEMENT
product, packaging

CROSS-DOCK
WAREHOUSING

INVESTMENT IN
FLEXIBILITY NOT
INVENTORY

RISK POOLING

STOCKPOINT
PACKAGING

CHANNEL SELECTION

PRINCIPLES

The 'TRIPLE A' CHAIN
AGILE, ADAPTABLE, ALIGNED

3 Day Car PRINCIPLES

QUICK
RESPONSE,
FLOW TO
CUSTOMERS

QUICK RESPONSE and ECR
EPOS, EDI, Web, B2B, RFID

SUPPLY CHAIN
CONCEPT
(Chains, not
Companies compete)

"CO-OPETITION"

TOC and HP Measures
Throughput dollar days, inventory dollar days,
Inventory driven cost

SCHEDULE VISIBILITY and BULLWHIP Removal

KEY ACCOUNTS

MAPPING THE DISTRIBUTION CHAIN
to identify wastes, time barriers, push-pull boundary

INFORMATION

DISTRIBUTE for Flow

Distribution is the other half of the supply chain. The aim is to achieve quick response, pipeline flow with minimum waste. In reality many distribution systems are networks catering for particular customer types along selected channels. Today it is recognised that supply chains compete, not companies.

Principles

The 'Triple A' chain, states the objectives as being agile, adaptable and aligned. *Agile* means adequate capacity for flexibility. *Adaptable* means an ability to cope with changes in mix and demand. *Aligned* means aligned with corporate objectives such as speed, or cost, or customisation.

The Three Day Car project established the following principles:

- Only build to customer order
- Book orders directly into assembly slots
- Make demand visible throughout the entire supply chain
- Minimise complexity whilst maintaining choice – by, for example, using the postponement or 'variety as late as possible' principle
- Proactively manage the flow of orders – fill demand troughs with less urgent orders, cut demand peaks with pricing
- Optimise profit across the entire supply chain – avoid winners and losers, share costs and opportunities – 'supply chains compete, not companies'.

Flow and inventory

The idea is to flow, not to warehouse. Cross docking shifts products from one truck to several delivery vehicles, so that inventory is warehoused for hours not days or weeks. Flow is aided by selecting appropriate channels, perhaps one for large customers, another for fast moving, a third for small customers. Flow may be aided by postponement in product (assembling at the last moment) or packaging (by customer type or language). A general principle is investment in flexibility rather than inventory; for instance in changeover, in transport, in capacity.

The ideal is to supply no-more and no-less, working under pull not push. This can only be achieved by a long-term end-to-end effort along the chain in the adoption of lean techniques and principles. Forcing lean by insisting on minimal buffers prevents game playing and amplification effects, and encourages the chain to work at the customer's rate. Where warehousing is necessary, inventory can still be reduced by "Risk Pooling", whereby local warehouse inventory is *virtually* centralised and some closed. Although inventory reduction takes place the penalty may be in response time. However, inventory and other flexibility savings may mean that more costly quick distribution still pays.

Stockpoint packaging tries to minimise the costs of stacking shelves and material handling by packing product in final display form, perhaps on roller pallets.

A Final Word: THE SEVEN P's – building on Jeffrey Liker

PROBLEM SOLVING	Surface and solve using PDCA; Learn
PARTNERS	The Supply Chain competes, not only the company
PROCEDURES	Standard work; capable machines
PROCESS	End-to-end value stream focus
PRODUCT	Product - service bundles that satisfy needs, now and in the future
PEOPLE	The bedrock; develop and grow them
PHILOSOPHY	Long term, consistent message

Information

This is key. Quick Response linkages with EPOS terminals or internet allow true customer demands to be communicated. B2B e-business is uncovering huge opportunity for speed and waste reduction. Related is schedule visibility, schedule stability and removal of the "bullwhip" effect which can also lead to huge savings. See the separate section on demand management. An associated step is to map the supply or distribution chain, particularly to identify wastes and the point where Push meets Pull. How it can be made to move upstream in future. The "co-opetition" concept allows competitors to co-operate for mutual benefit against outsiders but still to compete. Examples are common standards, trains vs. airlines, national distribution vs. international competition. Preparation for order receipt is a form of changeover reduction in distribution whereby maximum preparation for both physical and information flows is made in advance of receipt. Examples are customs pre-clearance and synchronised operations with fruit picking. Key account management extends the supplier partnership concepts to key customers. Both sides win.

Two measures are useful. *Throughput dollar days* measures the potential of lost sales by accumulating the cost of inventory only when it drops below a pre-defined level. *Inventory dollar days* accumulates the value of the item multiplied by the length of time spent in the chain, and encourages flow, particularly for high end items. These two measures work together, and were suggested by Goldratt.

Finally, beware RFID, radio frequency identification. RFID is a great advance on inventory tracking, reducing errors and waste. It works well with bar codes and ERP. However, it may also make keeping inventory too easy, when the real thing to do is to reduce and to flow products.

SELECTED FURTHER READING

Lean

John Bicheno, *The New Lean Toolbox,* PICSIE Books, 2004

Jeffrey Liker, *The Toyota Way,* McGraw Hill, 2004

Jeffrey Liker and David Meier, *The Toyota Way Fieldbook,* McGraw Hill, 2005

Ron Mascitelli, *Building a Project-Driven Enterprise,* Technology Perspectives, 2002

Michael Kennedy, *Product Development for the Lean Enterprise,* Oaklea Press, 2003

Wallace Hopp and Mark Spearman, *Factory Physics,* Second Ed, McGraw Hill, 2000

Brian Maskell and Bruce Baggaley, *Practical Lean Accounting,* Productivity, 2004

John Seddon, *Freedom from Command and Control,* Vanguard, 2003

David Simchi-Levi et al, *Designing and Managing the Supply Chain,* McGraw Hill, 2003

John Nicolas, *Competitive Manufacturing Management,* McGraw Hill, 1998.

James Womack and Daniel Jones, *Lean Solutions,* Simon and Schuster, 2005

Six Sigma and Quality

John Bicheno and Philip Catherwood, *Six Sigma and the Quality Toolbox,* PICSIE Books, 2005

Howard Gitlow and David Levine, *Six Sigma for Green Belts and Champions,* FT Prentice Hall, 2005

C Martin Hinckley, *Make No Mistake!,* Productivity, 2001

TRIZ

Darrell Mann, *Hands-on Systematic Innovation,* CREAX/IFR Press, 2002

TPM

Nick Rich and Dennis McCarthy, *Lean TPM,* Butterworth Heinemann, 2004

Games

The Buckingham Lean Game, PICSIE Books, 2000

The Buckingham Heijunka Game, PICSIE Books, 2006

The Buckingham Housing (Lean Service) Game, PICSIE Books

The Lean Leap Supply Chain Game, PICSIE Books, 2002

The Deming Red Bead Game, The Deming Forum